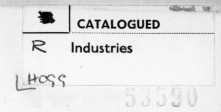

HAMMER & TONGS

Blacksmithery down the Ages

Hammer & Tongs

Blacksmithery down the Ages

GARRY HOGG

Drawings by Peter Chadwick

HUTCHINSON OF LONDON

HUTCHINSON & CO. (*Publishers*) LTD
178–202 Great Portland Street, London, W.1

London Melbourne Sydney
Auckland Bombay Toronto
Johannesburg New York

★

First published 1964

*This book has been set in Baskerville type face. It has
been printed in Great Britain by The Anchor Press,
Ltd., in Tiptree, Essex, on Antique Wove paper.*

Acknowledgements

I WOULD like to acknowledge my indebtedness to the following for their kind permission to quote from, or in other respects make use of, their work:

Mr Raymond Lister and his publishers, George Bell & Sons Ltd, *Decorative Wrought Ironwork in Great Britain*; Messrs Chapman & Hall Ltd, publishers of J. A. R. Stevenson's *The Din of a Smithy*; Messrs Faber & Faber Ltd, publishers of Mr G. E. Evans's *Horse in the Furrow*.

The words of 'The Viking Song' were written by David McKee Wright, whom unfortunately I have been unable to trace.

I am grateful also to the following for supplying the half-tone illustrations:

Lieutenant-Colonel R. Myddelton, who most kindly had a new photograph of the gates of Chirk Castle specially taken for me; the Rural Industries Bureau, for three photographs (and much useful information); the Warden and Fellows of New College, Oxford; the Dean and Chapter of Westminster Abbey; the Master and Fellows of Trinity College, Cambridge, and the Victoria and Albert Museum.

GARRY HOGG

Contents

Illustrations

I

Vulcan and company

ONE winter's evening some time before the turn of last century an ageing country blacksmith was sitting by the fireside in his cottage next door to the smithy. He was feeling tired. And this was not the first evening he had spent, sitting there opposite his wife, increasingly conscious that his muscles were complaining.

Time was, he reflected, when he could have swung his heavy hammer from daybreak to dusk, and still have felt fresh enough to go out and ridge his potatoes, plant a few rows of beans or do a little rabbit-poaching for the pot. But not lately. For the past good many months, when he had laid down his tools, dowsed the fire and locked the smithy door behind him, he had been well content to sit down and enjoy his tea, then light his pipe and put his feet up for the rest of the short evening before he went to bed.

It must be, he reluctantly admitted to himself at last, that he was growing old. It was a thought that had not struck him before, even when his daughter's children paid their occasional visits to the cottage and he dandled his twin grandsons on his knee. Never before, even to himself, had he admitted that he might be growing old. The thought disturbed him. He looked across at his elderly wife, placidly knitting on the other side of the fire as she always did in the evenings. And then his eyes strayed to the bulky old family Bible, from which he was in the habit of reading a chapter every evening before going to bed. He put on his steel-rimmed spectacles, and then opened it at random. Or perhaps not quite at random, for the passage his eyes lit on was one that he had read before, many times; it was one that had a special significance for him, that he felt might have been written about him:

> The vapour of the fire wasteth his flesh; the smith fighteth with the heat of the furnace; the noise of the hammer and the anvil is ever in his ears, and his eyes look upon the thing he maketh; he setteth his mind to finish his work, and watcheth it. . . .

He pondered long over the words, nodding his head slowly as he went over them in his mind. Then he looked about him for a piece of paper, drew a stub of pencil from his pocket, pulled the oil lamp a little nearer to him, and its yellow flame showed his brow furrowed in thought. At length he put his stub of pencil to the paper and, very slowly, with much scratching out and starting again, began to write.

His task took him the whole evening. Now and then his wife looked up from her knitting, surprised and a little puzzled by her husband's absorption in an unwonted activity. However, she said nothing, contenting herself with a fond smile, knowing that all in good time he would tell her what he was about. At last she saw him lay down his pencil and fold the sheet of paper into four. He made to slip it into the page of the Bible from which he had been reading, but then changed his mind. He unfolded the paper once again, smoothed it out flat on the table and looked across at her.

'I've just wrote something, Maggie,' he said, hesitantly. 'Shall I read it out to you?'

His wife laid down her knitting and folded her hands in her lap, expectant. Then, slowly, with much emphasis and very solemnly, he read out to her the lines he had written down with so much effort:

'My Fire's extinct, My Forge decayed,
And in the dust my Vice is laid;
My Coal is spent, my Iron's gone,
My Nails are drawn, my Work is done;
My Fire-dried Corpse lies here at Rest;
My Soul, like Smoke, soars to the Blest.'

There was silence in the snug, firelit kitchen when he had finished. Then, very simply, the blacksmith said: 'I'd like them words put on my tombstone, Maggie, when I'm gone.' That was all. He folded the sheet of paper once more and placed it carefully within the pages of the Bible which had given him his inspiration. Then he tapped out his pipe on the top bar of the grate and rose creakily to his feet, stiff from his long spell of concentration. It was time to go to bed.

In due course, though not as soon as he expected, the blacksmith died. His wife took the folded paper from the Bible and gave it to the local stonemason, asking him to carve the words her husband had written on the stone that was to mark his grave. It is there to this day, one of the small company of tilted, lichen-clad gravestones in a country churchyard.

The composer of those lines was probably a better smith than poet, handier with hammer and tongs than with pencil and paper; but he was, like most country manual workers of his day, a pious man. He had been accustomed to read his Bible all his life, and it was natural to him, as it had been to John Bunyan, the tinsmith from Bedfordshire, two centuries earlier, to express himself in simple parables such as those which had been the only means of communicating abstract ideas to unlettered men and women two thousand years before his day.

So, the 'Fire' of which he wrote was both the 'furnace' to which the biblical writer had referred and his own 'spark of

life'; his 'Forge' was his heart; his 'Vice' was not only the
daily one in use on his bench but such sinfulness as he
humbly believed he might have been guilty of. Now, he felt,
his work was done; his body, that had been subjected all his
life long to the 'heat of the furnace', was dying, while his
soul, he trusted, would rise to heaven as the smoke of his
forge had risen into the heavens throughout the long working
days in his smithy.

Though he did not realize it, that humble country blacksmith was writing not only his own epitaph but, in a way,
that of a whole race of craftsmen; the blacksmiths who have
figured prominently in the whole civilized world for
thousands of years, but who, in their traditional guise at any
rate, are today a dying race. Or, if not actually a dying race,
at least one that in recent years has been forced by the irre-
sistible pressure of change in our way of life either to adapt
themselves wholesale to new demands or to abandon altogether one of the oldest—some would say the oldest without
question—and most fundamental crafts developed and
practised by man.

It is certainly no exaggeration to refer to blacksmithing as
a craft of immense antiquity. Blacksmithing was well
established in Britain long before Julius Caesar's legions set
foot on her shores. In Syria, in Egypt and elsewhere in the
Middle and Far East, the craft of smelting and manipulating copper, bronze and iron was understood at least
four thousand years ago, and probably earlier even than
that.

However great the damage and misery caused by warfare,
usually there is something of value to emerge as a result. It
was because of the interminable warfare between, for
example, the Hittites and their neighbours in the Middle
East that tribes were dispersed far afield, and so individual
craftsmen having a knowledge of the working of metals,

fleeing from the war-ravaged districts, spread south and west into Europe and brought with them their knowledge and individual skills. These were in time imparted to people who until then had been slower to reach a recognizable degree of civilization than their distant neighbours in the Middle and Far East.

Archaeologists digging among the ruined and long-abandoned cities of those ancient civilizations have found among the relics of the Assyrians, for instance, immense quantities of iron bars, weapons and tools, stored in rock vaults dry enough to have preserved them almost intact for close on three thousand years. The craft of manipulating metal, the inventiveness and adaptability of the Middle Eastern smiths, became available to the Celts; the Celts, diffused in various parts of Europe, eventually brought their knowledge and skill to our own shores round about the year 500 B.C.

Historically the smith has a long tradition. But recorded history was preceded by mythology, and the smith was an outstanding figure in the legends of remotest antiquity. He was a man who evoked from his fellow-men a degree of respect that is better described as reverence, or even awe. He was regarded as god-like in his powers, and in fact was often ranked among the pagan gods themselves, with a right to a place of his own in their various legendary abodes, whether on Mount Olympus or elsewhere.

In Greek mythology he was called Hephaestus, the wayward son of the great Zeus by his wife, the goddess Hera; by a link natural enough in simple minds, he was at once the god of fire as well as the god of iron. He was an artist-craftsman—as smiths have been all down the ages, and indeed remain today if they have been successful in over-coming economic difficulties and plying their ancient trade in this twentieth century. Hephaestus worked in many different metals, including gold. He fashioned the armour of Achilles and the thunderbolts of his father, Zeus; he fashioned the brazen fire-breathing bulls of Æetes that guarded the Golden Fleece; he created the golden images of beautiful handmaidens to serve the gods on Olympus; and he turned his mighty strength to the fashioning of a delicate and intricate necklace for Harmonia on the occasion of her marriage to Cadmus.

Whenever he had the chance he did what all his successors in the craft have always done: he combined the functional and utilitarian with the decorative. There was usually scope for this, for in those distant days, as for many centuries since, there always seemed to be time for the deployment of individual skills, for the indulgence of the artistic impulse in the craftsman. Homer, who delighted in detailed descriptive writing as well as in vigorous story-telling, gives us a memorable picture of the god-smith Hephaestus at work in his smithy. With the skilled support of his trained assistants, Hephaestus is fashioning a great shield: an object that is to combine the essential strength and toughness with the beauty which, in the craftsman's view, is hardly less important:

The bellows blew on the crucibles, sending deft blasts on every side, now to his labour, now to another's, however Hephaestus willed. The work went on. He threw bronze that decayeth not into the fire, together with tin, and precious gold, and silver too. Then he set on an anvil stand a great anvil, and took up a sturdy hammer in one hand while in the other he griped his tongs. So he fashioned a shield, great and strong. And then he set to adorning it all over, and giving to it a shining rim threefold and bright-gleaming, and also a baldrick of finely-fashioned silver . . .

Like most artists and craftsmen, Hephaestus seems to have been something of an individualist. For a time he was content to have his smithy on high Olympus among his fellow-gods. But he chafed at being at the constant beck and call of his father, and one day he revolted against authority. For his presumptuousness he was cast out. His fall was spectacular, for was he not the god of fire, as well as being the ·celestial blacksmith? It may well be that his great trajectory through the sky was the origin of the legends associated with meteors and shooting-stars.

For centuries past the poets of many countries have given expression to this belief, writing in many languages and infusing the basic story with their own native twists of fancy. John Milton was one poet whose imagination was stirred by the legend to write how Hephaestus fell from the heavens . . .

> Thrown by an angry Jove
> Sheer o'er the crystal battlements. From morn
> To noon he fell, from noon to dewy eve,
> A summer's day; and with the setting sun
> Dropped from the zenith, like a falling star,
> On Lemnos, the Aegean isle . . .

Others have said that Hephaestus fell for nine whole days and nights, so great was the distance between Olympus and the crawling world of ordinary men, and so powerful the arm of Zeus.

In any case, the rebel god-smith fell on to one of the myriad islands of the Greek Archipelago. There for a time he made his home. He burrowed deep into the ground, to be well out of sight of his father, and set up his smithy in the bowels of the earth. Then he called to his aid the stunted and misshapen creatures who already inhabited the island's dark and secret caverns, and trained them to be his new assistants. Later he removed to another island, taking with him his tools and tackle and as many of his helpers as he could coerce. Once more he established his smithy deep below

B

ground. The flames and smoke from his forge thrust upwards like great lurid tongues among the hill-tops; the continuous impact of his hammers on his anvils produced a subterranean rumbling that was deep and menacing and made itself felt as well as heard among the habitations of men on the surface, and even aboard the fishing vessels threading their way among the islands. There were active volcanoes in the area, but the islanders knew better: the rumblings they could hear, and the smoke and flames they could see, were proof that Hephaestus and his henchmen were hard at work deep down below the surface of the island on which they lived.

When the Greek mythology was temporarily replaced by that of the Romans, Hephaestus was renamed. Now he became Vulcan (see plate opposite page 32). This Roman god of iron and fire gave his name to these fire-breathing mountains: Volcanoes; Stromboli and Mount Etna are among the volcanoes beneath which it was firmly believed that the god-smith and his demon assistants hammered day and night on their subterranean anvils.

The same god-smith appears in the Old Testament book, Genesis, though now he is named Tubal-Cain, 'the first artificer in metal, the instructor of every artificer in brass and iron'. His successors were the smiths who forged the nine hundred chariots of iron used by Sisera, captain of the hosts serving the King of Canaan. A more cheerful character than Hephaestus and Vulcan, Tubal-Cain seems to have been— at any rate if we are to believe what the poet Charles Mackay wrote about him:

> And he sang, 'Hurrah for my handiwork!'
> And the red sparks lit the air;
> Not alone for the blade
> Was the bright steel made,
> And he fashioned the first plough-share.

There is hardly a mythology in any part of the world in which this ancient belief in an all-powerful fire-god-smith does not appear. Nor is it difficult to see why this should be so. After all, fire—or rather the ability to create and control fire—was among the first and certainly the greatest of Man's early achievements. The utilization of this newly discovered element in the fashioning of tools and, still more important, of weapons was the first and logical development: Man harnessed a powerful ally, and as a result immediately became infinitely more powerful than any neighbour whose skill and invention were less than his own. With a tool of iron, or even of bronze, a man could fell a tree or till the soil far more rapidly, and with far less effort, than his neighbour whose only tool was a flint axe or a pointed hardwood stake. With a sword and a shield a man could go confidently into battle, knowing that he would triumph over an enemy armed only with sling or club.

So, throughout the Morning of Time, legend speaks of the man of fire and iron, striding like a colossus among his fellows, admired, reverenced, feared. In ancient Greece his name was Hephaestus; the Romans called him Vulcan; in the Old Testament he is Tubal-Cain. There is no immediate and obvious connection among them; no similarity in their names, even though their skill and exploits were much the same. Later, though, the name given to this fire-god-smith took on a shape that suggested that each was an echo of the other; the scattered communities of Europe developed their individual variants, but the fundamentals remained the same, and the names were, so to speak, interchangeable.

Britain had Wayland—'Wayland the Smith'—who flourished on the Sussex and Berkshire Downs where our earliest communities settled. In the early mythology of France his name appears as Galland; the parallel is as close as that of Guillaume and William today. The early Germanic tribes

called him Wieland, closer still to our Wayland in appearance and sound. And Scandinavian mythology—in many
respects the most unusual and exciting of them all—knew
him as Volundr.

Volundr was the Norse hero-blacksmith who alone knew
the secret of forging armour and weapons which endowed
the wearer with the priceless gift of invulnerability. According to the Norsemen he was one of three brothers married
to Valkyries. While two of the brothers roamed the world,
Volundr stayed at home in his valley, practising his craft,
selling his priceless wares to the highest bidder and so
amassing a gigantic fortune.

His wealth became so enormous that it aroused the
covetousness of a Scandinavian chieftain, Nidudr, who by
an unexpected stroke of luck succeeded in separating him
from his magic weapons just long enough to capture him.
Without more ado, he tied him up and transferred him to
a remote island, where he was freed from his bonds on
condition that he would in future work for him alone,
forging armour and magic weapons with which to equip an
army capable of destroying all Nidudr's enemies. To make
doubly sure that Volundr would never be able to escape from
the island, he hamstrung him. Thenceforward the captured
smith was permanently bent and crooked, so that his legs
were practically useless to him. However, he had not lost his
former strength of arm and shoulder, which were phenom-
enally strong; and he had lost nothing of his skill.

Volundr, the legend recounts, lay low, working in his
smithy, biding his time, planning a gruesome revenge. His
revenge, when at last the chance came, was marked by the
cruelty and callousness which is an integral part of these
traditional sagas, as of the ballads that followed on their
heels; and to him it was sweet indeed. He murdered
Nidudr's sons. Having murdered them—a mere preliminary

to his revenge—he scalped them, cleaned and polished their skulls, and mounted them in gold. Their eyes he carefully preserved and, by some peculiar magic known only to himself, transmuted them into living gems. Their teeth he extracted from the jaws and fashioned into an elaborate necklace. Then he fashioned for himself a means by which, when the crucial moment came, he could make his escape.

On the chosen day he presented Nidudr with his children's gold-mounted skulls; their mother with the living eye-gems; and their sister with the elaborate necklace made of her dead brothers' teeth. He gave himself just long enough to tell, gloatingly, the detailed story of how he had caught and killed the boys; then, using a pair of magic wings that he had designed and fashioned secretly at night in his smithy for just this purpose, he soared aloft through the window and escaped to his own territory.

Variants of his story can be traced through most of these mythologies. The names may be different, the details vary; but fundamentally it is always the same story: that of the hero-smith (often more than a little of a villain) in conflict with other gods and lesser men, triumphing unexpectedly and dramatically because of his expert knowledge of the properties of fire and iron and his skill in manipulating metal, whether precious, like silver and gold, or base, like bronze and iron.

In Norse mythology (as in the Teutonic, for that matter) there is often momentary confusion among the characters, and exploits are ascribed to them which may be contradicted elsewhere. But there is so much vigour in those inter-related sagas that it bursts out in all sorts of forms, and inspires poets to write verses and composers to set the verses to music, so that we ourselves are tempted to burst into song inspired by the rhythm of the hammers on the anvils of those legendary figures. Few of these songs possess a greater vitality and evocative power than that written by David McKee Wright and set to music by Coleridge-Taylor, the famous 'Viking Song':

Clang clang clang on the anvil,
In the smithy by the dark North Sea;
Is it Thor that is smiting with the hammer,
Is it Odin with the leather on his knee?

Clang clang clang on the anvil,
And the flames of the forges leap.
Old Thor, with his red beard glowing,
Has his eyes on the furrows of the deep.

Clang clang clang on the anvil,
On the margin of the soul-bright sea;
Is it Odin that is watching in the shadows,
Is it Thor where the sparks fly free?

Clang clang clang on the anvil,
(For the forge of the Viking may not sleep);
Clang clang clang on the anvil,
(For the blood of the Viking may not sleep).

On the anvil, that 'base metal', iron, was hammered and forged. It is in the manipulating and fashioning of this so-called 'base' metal down the ages that the blacksmith's finest achievements are to be seen mirrored.

It may be called base metal, but strangely enough it has always been regarded as something possessing magic properties, and therefore in certain respects as more valuable even than the precious metals worked by goldsmiths and silversmiths. This may at first seem surprising: after all, iron is the most commonplace of metals; scrap-iron merchants usually have their dingy, down-at-heel yards in the more squalid districts of the town; the cry 'Any old iron?' is familiar in back streets; but few people are so optimistic as to expect to be paid for ironware they have done with, and in fact they are usually glad enough to have it removed from their sight without being charged for the service!

If anyone today were to suggest that there exists the element of magic in a piece of iron he would be laughed at. Nevertheless it is more than possible that the very people who laughed at him would be among the first to pick up a cast horseshoe if they happened to come across this unlikely object lying in the road. Having picked it up, the chances are that they would proceed to nail the horseshoe to the door of a garden shed, or under the eaves of their house—'just for luck'. In all probability, too, they would make sure that they nailed the shoe to the door with the points upwards.

If asked why they fastened it that way up they might look momentarily puzzled, but would eventually answer: 'So that the luck doesn't drain out of it.' They might say this rather shamefacedly, as though expecting to be mocked for what they had done; but the very fact that they had nailed the horseshoe to the door at all, quite apart from the care they had taken to put it the right way up, is clear evidence that somewhere deep down in their consciousness there still lurked an ancient superstition—one of the longest-lived and most potent of all popular superstitions—that to find a cast horseshoe is to expect good luck; and to hang it (right way up) is to guarantee that the good luck will remain with the house and its occupants.

Ancient peoples, however, had no such feelings of shame or self-consciousness. For them, a man who worked in iron was a man to be held in awe; he was someone greater than themselves, hardly less than a god. Indeed, he might even be descended from the gods—Hephaestus, perhaps, or Vulcan. He possessed skills unknown to the ordinary mortal;

he could tame to his use an element that induced fear in lesser men: Fire—that good servant but bad master. Moreover, he worked in a metal that could resist fire, could be shaped by fire, forged and tempered into swords and spearheads and other weapons by the power of fire controlled and mastered by a smith.

What is more, the metal he worked with was of strange, unexplained origin; so, like all things inexplicable, it was to be regarded with awe amounting to fear. The first iron encountered by Man was meteoric iron. Because it appeared unexpectedly, often in somewhat menacing shapes and in the unlikeliest of places, it was believed to have been hurled out of the heavens by the angry gods. The Egyptians called it 'The Stone from Heaven' and associated it with the terrible god of storms whom they knew as Seth. Though they also called it 'The Gift from the Gods', they nevertheless feared it; it was a very long time before any Egyptian metal-worker dared handle it.

The metal-workers of those days, in that country, were in fact goldsmiths, for gold had been known to the Egyptians long before iron. So rarely did these fragments of meteoric iron come their way that the metal was regarded as precious, both by those who worked it and by their despotic and avaricious employers, the successive Pharaohs. For them it ranked higher even than Nubian gold. That it was so highly esteemed is clearly proved by the fact that graves excavated by archaeologists in El Gerzeh and dated by them as far back as 4000 B.C. have been found to contain beads made from this meteoric iron, laid there with other personal treasures to accompany the dead into the after-life.

It is not surprising that the metal-workers who were the first to experiment with the manipulation of this newly encountered 'precious metal' were careful to keep to themselves such discoveries as they made in the course of their

early experimenting. What they learned—often the hard and
painful way—they kept secret, just as the African witch-
doctor cherishes the accumulated knowledge that makes him
powerful among the fellow-members of his tribe. The men
who later handled this metal, the original 'ironsmiths' who
came to be known as 'blacksmiths' (as opposed to goldsmiths, coppersmiths, tinsmiths, silversmiths) because this
new metal was black, cherished their knowledge and developing skill, maintaining among themselves a close-knit
brotherhood, or crafthood.

They encouraged an atmosphere of secrecy to develop
among them; they welcomed the aura of mystery that
seemed to surround them and to provide an invisible
but potent barrier between themselves and other, lesser,
men. This gave them power over their fellows; it promised
wealth, because they had something to offer that no one else
could provide. They could name their own terms for the
forging of weapons, armour or tools; and the articles they
forged out of this 'Stone from Heaven' inevitably acquired a
unique property, of which the fortunate owner would be
able to claim sole possession. The material of which it was
made possessed the double merit of being sacred—in that it
came direct from the heavens; and valuable—in that it was
rare and hard to come by.

It was only a small step from that realization to the claim
that anything whatsoever fashioned out of this rare and
sacred metal possessed the property of magic; equally, of
course, the man who alone among his fellows could forge
such an object must automatically possess magical powers
peculiar to himself.

It is a far cry from the discovery of meteoric iron, from the
forging of Jove's thunderbolts by Hephaestus in the bowels
of the earth, from the depositing of ornamental iron beads
in Egyptian graves, to the epitaph on the tombstone of the

pious country blacksmith of nearly a century ago. In the thousands of years of history and prehistory that have elapsed, the notion of magic has gradually slipped away from the blacksmith's craft; the blacksmith himself has shed his cloak of mystery like an outworn garment. Very few blacksmiths indeed, if you were to talk to them about the awe in which their remote ancestors were held, would have the slightest idea what you were talking about. To them, the handling of iron, its forging into horseshoes, railings, inn-signs or ornamental gates, is just an everyday job to be undertaken, completed and paid for.

Today there are fewer blacksmiths at work than there were at any time in the past. So far as our own country is concerned their heyday was probably during the Middle Ages. Some historians put it in the thirteenth and fourteenth centuries, though most knowledgeable people agree that work was being produced for several centuries after that which was every bit as fine as that of the smiths who were at their anvils in Geoffrey Chaucer's day. Even now, in this mid-twentieth century, there are blacksmiths who can turn out work comparable in every way with the finest products of what is sometimes referred to as 'The Smiths' Age'. You have only to look at some of the modern gates, inn-signs, ornamental railings and other examples of the blacksmith's craft to recognize the truth of that statement.

The sober fact is, however, that whereas a century or so ago blacksmiths could be counted by the thousand, today that number has dwindled to a mere fraction. It is nine centuries since William the Conqueror compiled the Domesday Book. One item in this survey of Britain's population and their occupations in A.D. 1086 mentions casually that in the small town of Hereford there were six smithies in full blast. Two hundred years later, when Edward I was on the throne, there were no fewer than seventy-two smithies in the small area of the Forest of Dean alone. From those smithies came the gigantic tally of fifty thousand horseshoes for the chargers that carried Richard Lionheart and his knights on his crusade to the Holy Land in A.D. 1190. On the opposite side of the country there was the ancient town of Colchester, the Romans' Camulodunum. Today it is a sizable town of over sixty thousand inhabitants; in the Middle Ages it was not much more than an over-grown village. But even in those far-off days it gave full employment for no fewer than ten smithies.

It is probably true to say that until the turn of last century —about the time, that is, when the ageing blacksmith picked up his stub of pencil and laboriously composed his own epitaph—there was hardly a village, hardly even a hamlet, however small, that had not its own smithy. This was the smithy of popular song: the centre of local gossip, the favourite meeting-place of cronies who enjoyed a natter in the half-light while the smith and his mate swung their hammers and made the bright sparks fly in the murky air. It was the rural smithy that the poet Longfellow immortalized in 1841 when he wrote 'The Village Blacksmith':

Under a spreading chestnut tree
  The village smithy stands;
The smith, a mighty man is he,
  With large and sinewy hands;
And the muscles of his brawny arms
  Are strong as iron bands.

Week in, week out, from morn till night,
  You can hear his bellows blow;
You can hear him swing his heavy sledge
  With measured beat and slow,
Like a sexton ringing the village bell
  When the evening sun is low . . .

It is true that the poet was writing of a village smithy near his own home, in Massachusetts; but village smithies the world over have much in common.

How many true smithies can be found in this country today it is not easy to estimate. Most big engineering firms, of course, have a blacksmiths' department in which repairs can be carried out and certain types of tool be re-tempered. Most large quarries have their own smithies on or near the site, the smiths being employed almost entirely in sharpening and tempering heavy tools such as crowbars, wedges and cold chisels, setting up springs, welding cracked links, hooks and shackles, and so forth. But these are departments of big organizations rather than the smithy as we usually think of it, as Longfellow wrote of it: the country or village smithy where the smith and his mate work for themselves, making horseshoes, repairing ploughshares and harrows and coulters and other basic implements essential to the farming community surrounding the village. It is this type of smithy that today is hardest of all to find, and best worth visiting if you ever have the good fortune to find it.

It has been said that before the war there were still two or three thousand smithies scattered up and down and across the country. If that figure is correct it would almost certainly be made up largely of the smithies that are in fact no more than departments of big industrial concerns; the true smithy, the 'one-man-and-his-mate' establishment, formerly to be found in every village, however small and remote, whether graced by the traditional spreading chestnut tree or not, is surely dying out.

You may still find it, disguised as a garage where oxy-acetylene welding equipment is more in evidence than hammer and tongs and anvil (see plate opposite page 33). It may appear in the form of a depot for agricultural machinery, identifiable by the clutter of tractors, binders,

hay-tedders, balers and so on outside the double doors
through which, only a generation or so ago, the plough
horse used to be led to be fitted with a new set of heavy shoes.

It may still show, as one old smithy I often pass, just off
the Great North Road, still shows, a giant horseshoe twelve
feet high, picked out in black-painted brickwork and
spanning the wide double doors—unmistakable sign of the
owner's original occupation when horses and horse-drawn
vehicles were still the only form of transport between
London and Edinburgh. But the chances are that nowadays
the ancient smithy is no more than a petrol station, or a
wayside café and snack-bar catering for long-distance lorry
drivers plying between north and south. Perhaps the fact
that the giant horseshoe on the façade of such buildings is,
as in this particular case, usually designed with its points
turned downward, instead of right way up, explains why
this sorry change has come about: the good luck that
would have been brought by the rightly-mounted shoe,
relic of the magic 'Stone from Heaven', just has not come its
way.

The likeliest district in which, in this mid-twentieth
century, to come across the traditional type of smithy—the
smithy in which the shoeing of horses is the main and thriving
activity—is one in which riding-schools and hunting-stables
flourish; one in which, therefore, there will be a continuous
flow of horses and ponies into and out of the smithy yard and
through its double doors.

I know of a number of such smithies. One in particular is
to be found on the Kent-Sussex border not many miles from
my home. It was established many generations ago. The
present smith—son, or it may be grandson, of the first smith
to work there—is over eighty years old. His son, a busy
farrier with more than three hundred horses 'on his books',
is more than half his age. His mate is middle-aged too. But

there is no son to carry on the trade when, in thirty or forty
years' time, the farrier downs tools for the last time.

It is the most flourishing smithy I know. Often when I
have a morning or afternoon to spare I slip away from home,
hurry over the few miles that separate us and gladly enter
the smithy through the wide doors, surmounted by a four-
foot 'horseshoe' mounted the right way up, guarantee of
good workmanship and the maintenance of an ancient
tradition. There I can always find shoeing in progress, for
there are riding-schools and hunting-stables for miles around,
and this smith has a fine reputation for workmanship, and
horses are brought in to him from a radius of many miles
away in all directions. As I watch him at work I recapture
afresh each time something of the mystery and magic that
have always imbued this ancient craft.

2

The heart of the smithy

THE dominant feature of every smithy, of course, is the forge itself. It is the focal point, the living heart of the blacksmith's daily life. Having entered perhaps from bright sunshine, your eyes may take a few moments to adjust themselves to the dim light which pervades the interiors of most smithies. But maybe at the very moment you come in the smith has taken hold of the handle of his bellows and you hear that curious, inimitable 'bubble-in-the-throat' sound which the old-fashioned bellows always produce. Almost immediately a small glow appears in the heart of the forge: the breath of life has been restored to it.

By now your eyes have become accustomed to the half-light and you can begin to take in the principal features of the smithy. First there is the forge—which the smith will refer to as his Hearth, or Fire. It consists of a square frame-work, usually of brick but sometimes of iron. This stands at roughly table height from the brick-laid or stone floor, and the height is important, since in the course of a full working day the smith may have transferred a total weight of a ton or more of pieces of iron from anvil to forge and from forge to anvil and back again, for heating, hammering and tempering; every extra inch of unnecessary lift involves him in unnecessary muscular effort.

On this brick table the smith builds his Pit, or Bed, of coke, or of Smithy Breeze made up of particles of fuel generally known, because of their size, as Beans. Over this

Blacksmith's Hearth

fire-bed, or pit, hangs a Cowl, or Canopy, or Hood, either
of brick or of sheet iron, broad enough at its open base to
spread well out over the hearth and tapering upwards into
the chimney. It is designed to lead the smoke and the fumes
from hot metal away from the forge and out into the
open air.

In front of the hearth and braced against the brickwork is a
cast-iron trough generally known as the Bosh, kept full of
water in which hot iron can be Dowsed or Quenched for

Vulcan, the legendary blacksmith, at work. From an old engraving

A modern smithy

(Rural Industries Bureau)

tempering. In this, too, any pair of tongs that with sustained use over the fire-pit may have become overheated will also be dowsed, to be restored once more to a normal working temperature. There is usually an iron rail fitted to the upper edge of the brickwork and running the whole length of one or more sides; over this rail there hang the smith's armoury of tongs, handles downwards, ready for immediate use. Behind, or on the third side, and often in a recess beneath the cowl within easy reach, there is a small fuel-bunker from which he can quickly replenish his fire.

A blacksmith's fire is always small and concentrated. In a fire-pit perhaps four or five feet square the actual fire which heats the metal may well be no more than a few inches across. Surrounding it, however, is the as yet unburnt fuel, which he can rake in towards the centre at need. Lying across the corner of the hearth will be his Slice—a long-handled, light-weight, near-flat shovel with which he scoops up a handful of breeze and manœuvres it exactly to the point where he is developing his heat. Alongside it there lies a small rake, or Fire-hook, for extracting clinker and regulating the depth of the glowing breeze. One other accessory lies conveniently to hand: a home-made brush of twigs with which he can deftly flick a spray of cold water from the bosh on to his fuel when he wants to decrease the area of intense heat with the least possible waste of time. He may use an old tin instead, but most smiths find that the old-fashioned bundle of twigs is handiest—a well-tried and cheaply-made accessory.

The hearth is alive; life is breathed into it by the Bellows. You will hear the bellows though you may not always see them, for they are usually mounted in a recess behind the hearth itself, which projects well forward in the smithy, sometimes so far forward that it is possible to walk right round it. The advantage of this siting is that two forges can

C

be built, back to back, and two smiths can then work them
at the same time. Alternatively, two forges may be side by
side, like twin beds standing out from the same wall, and their
twin canopies will draw the fumes and smoke upwards to
unite in a single chimney and be carried away thus above
the smithy roof.

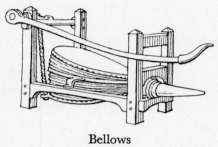

Bellows

It is not known who invented the principle of the bellows
—without which no really great heat can be obtained on an
open hearth. Until the principle of the forced draught was
understood it was impossible to melt or smelt or fuse metals.
If great heat was called for, then a great fire had to be built;
and if the fire was on a large scale it became too hot to
approach, difficult to utilize and quite likely impossible to
control.

Conjecture and speculation suggest that someone in far-off
times built a furnace on the slope of a windswept hill and
discovered to his surprise and delight that the wind funnel-
ling through a chink at the back of his furnace blew it into
unexpected heat. More imaginative and intelligent, perhaps,
than his fellows, he divined the explanation and proceeded
to experiment with what had been discovered by chance.
The phenomenon was repeated, again and again; when the
wind funnelled through a cleft in the rock behind his hearth
it produced a degree of heat he had never known before. The

next step was to produce the wind when, and where, he required it.

It is certainly true that this method was known some thousands of years ago, for there exist tomb paintings of ancient Egyptians operating a primitive form of bellows and producing the desirable forced draught. Proof that the method evolved, though primitive, was effective lies in the fact that archaeologists have found objects forged from metal that could never have been produced at all had not the metal-workers, Egyptians and others in the Middle East known how to super-heat the materials they worked in.

Their bellows were probably made from a goatskin sewn up in the form of a bag, such as that of a water-carrier, with a small opening into which either a hollow reed or a clay tube was inserted. The paintings show that the bellows operator had two such goatskin bags and stood with one foot on each. He grasped in each hand a thong attached to the upper surface of the skins. Rather like someone treading water, or marking time, he operated these makeshift bellows by transferring his weight in turn from one foot to the other. As each goatskin took his weight the air inside was expelled through the pipe and into the fire; as he removed his weight, and hauled upwards on the cord he held, the goatskin expanded again in readiness for the next bout of pressure. It was a very simple device, by no means a hundred per cent efficient, but at the same time not very exacting of effort. All the operator had to do was to sway lightly and rhythmically from one foot to the other, and keep each cord taut as he did so. The device is to be found in use among primitive tribes today where inventiveness is slight but manpower abundant.

The twin goatskin bags were in effect Double-acting bellows, whereas a single goatskin, squeezed under the foot or beneath the arm (like bagpipes), was a forerunner of the Single-acting bellows. As long ago as the Middle Ages in this country the blacksmith was equipped with both types of bellows, though nothing so primitive as inflated goatskins would serve his requirements. The type of bellows he used then he uses still, though the electrically-powered fan is gradually gaining ground with progressive-minded smiths. The traditional type of bellows somewhat resembles a large concertina, built into a sturdy wood-and-metal frame and installed horizontally behind or alongside the forge. It may be circular or pear-shaped and have as many as six or more leather folds one above the other.

The great advantage of the double-acting bellows is that the Blast is produced by both the upward and the downward swing of the bellows arm, and so is continuous, not intermittent. The smith can therefore rely on a constant and unvarying heat. On a small job he may operate the bellows himself, one hand grasping the tongs that hold the metal in the hearth, the other the smooth cow-horn which is the traditional grip on the end of the ash handle. The curve of the horn, you will notice, is downward, for the only pressure required is in that direction, a counter-weight bringing the bellows up again, discharging the blast and refilling them with air at the same time.

If the smith is engaged on a two-handed job, however, then the bellows must be operated by someone else. One of the pleasantest ways I know of spending an hour or two on a cold winter's afternoon is to invite oneself into a smithy and offer to act as bellows man. This is not a job to take on thoughtlessly; nor will the smith automatically accept your offer. For careless operation of the bellows can very quickly result in a spoilt Heat and the consequent undoing of the smith's work. An experienced blacksmith's mate knows exactly what degree of heat is required for any one of a hundred specific tasks, and produces this without spoken instruction. If he cannot do this, then he is not much use to the master smith.

The blacksmith talks of 'taking a four-inch heat' (or whatever it may be). He is not overmuch concerned with temperatures, expressed either in degrees Fahrenheit or centigrade; rather, he judges his heats by their colour. And he knows them also by name—strangely poetical names, sometimes, too.

There is, for example, Snowball Heat—the name he gives to what we would call white heat. This is the degree of heat he requires for the tricky operation of welding best-quality wrought iron. It reduces the iron to 'sponginess', which he will later restore to the requisite degree of hardness and the right texture by skilful hammering on the anvil. Next in order come the three degrees of welding heat. These are Full, Light, and Slippery, Greasy or Sweating. They are the heats most in demand, and with the hearth at such temperatures most of the standard operations are carried out: operations such as hammering iron to shape, for it is thus reduced to a softish, plastic consistency.

Near these welding heats, though still differing by a good many degrees, comes Cherry-Red, Dull Red or Blood-Red. The smith requires this temperature when he is on the last stage of a job that has been subjected already to the heats known as Bright Red or Bright Yellow: it has acquired its final shape but still needs smoothing, or finishing-off. Curiously enough, the smith also occasionally requires what he refers to as a Black Heat. It is used in finishing-off processes, such as giving an Oil or Matt surface to the forged metal. This heat is not visible in full daylight, or even in the half-light of the smithy; but the iron will be seen to be glowing very faintly if it is held for a moment in deep shadow.

Still another heat remains available to the blacksmith, also oddly named: Warm Heat. At this heat the metal is not hot enough to glow even in the darkest corner of the smithy. It is produced by passing the metal slowly to and fro through a very moderate fire; and the test for it is that it should be just too hot for even the tough, leathery palm and fingers of the smith to close upon. (You would be well advised not to try the test for Warm Heat yourself!) The smith uses this particular heat when 'setting up' springs, for it enables him to restore their original elasticity without depriving them of their temper.

Obviously highly skilled use of the bellows, as well as deft use of slice and rake and dowsing twigs, is necessary to obtain so many varied heats. To begin with, much depends on the construction of the actual hot-spot in the hearth: it must be neither so large as to disperse the heat and waste fuel, nor so small that it cannot include the whole of the metal to be treated. It must be close enough to the source of draught but not so close as to be scattered by too powerful blast from the bellows.

This blast is conveyed along a metal pipe, the last foot or so of which consists of a cast-iron pipe with thick walls and inside dimension of about one inch. Because the end of this tube is to be continuously in contact with very hot fuel it is frequently fitted with a water-filled 'sleeve', which helps to preserve it in the same way as water circulating in a car's cylinder-block protects the cylinders. The tube is known by several names, including Tuyère, Tewel, Tewel-iron and Tue-iron. It protrudes through the cast-iron back-plate of the fire-pit and directs the blast on to the work in hand.

The smith knows to within a fraction of an inch just where in that glowing heat of his fire-pit to hold and manipulate the piece of iron he is forging. In this he shows a skill that is not always recognized. Whereas a glass-blower, working with a needle-like, high-intensity jet of flame to shape a tube for some chemical experiment, can see the whole of his flame and his material at the same time, and confidently apply one to the other, or the user of an oxy-acetylene flame can direct it exactly on to his metal for spot-welding, the blacksmith has to work to a large extent by instinct and by feel: his hot-spot has depth as well as length and breadth; the object he is forging may be heavy to hold, cumbersome to manipulate; the draught may have to be varied, the temperature be built up or decreased as he works. It is one measure of his skill that he achieves his aims so consistently and—to the untutored eye—with such apparent ease.

More and more smiths in recent years have replaced their traditional leather bellows by electrically-driven fans and blowers. These, though less picturesque by far, and characterized by a high-pitched whine instead of the pleasant 'bubble-in-the-throat' sound, have two outstanding advantages: their blast can be regulated to a nicety and maintained constantly for an indefinite period; and they do not require manual operation. A touch of the air valve, a flick of the switch, and the requisite blast is there at the right strength from the very outset.

Few blacksmiths today would be reluctant to replace the centuries-old type of bellows by this simple and efficient modern type; it is the sentimentalist, who regards all things old as better than anything new, who cherishes the 'music' of the wheezy leathern bellows, which were repaired by Shakespeare's Flute, the bellows-mender in distant Athens, and the feel of the smooth, warm-to-the-touch cow-horn on the end of the bellows handle, who will deplore the advent of electricity and the amenities it introduces into the village smithy. Though understandable, this is really a foolish attitude of mind. For the smith has surrendered nothing of his inborn skill by accepting such mechanical aids; he has still to apply his accumulated expertise to every task he undertakes; but being freed from the unprofitable labour of swinging on the arm of his bellows he has that much extra in reserve for the processes that really demand skill and concentration.

However, the sentimentalist is not entirely alone in de-
ploring the passing of the traditional bellows. A noted West
Country blacksmith, specimens of whose wrought-iron work
are to be found in many parts of this country, and abroad
too, has stated categorically that he prefers these bellows to
the blast from the electrically-driven fan. He maintains—
and he should know, for he is a practising blacksmith of
long experience and a high reputation—that 'with such
bellows you can regulate the heat of your fire to better
advantage than you can with the less sensitive fan'. On jobs
that call for long periods of steadily maintained heat he
would probably agree that the electric fan has a great deal in
its favour; but it is also true that a quick, sure touch on the
handle of the leather bellows will produce a change of heat,
upwards or downwards in degree, more swiftly than the
adjustment of a switch or butterfly-valve.

*   *   *   *

Close by the forge, and indeed hardly less important,
stands the smith's anvil. The anvil is to the smith what the
wheel is to the potter, the easel to the artist or the bench to
the joiner or cabinet-maker: on it practically the whole of
his work is done.

To the uninitiated it may look no more than a rather
oddly shaped lump of black and pitted metal; in fact it is a
most skilfully designed and constructed object. Old illu-
minated manuscripts and other pictorial records show
medieval blacksmiths at work on a torpedo-shaped lump of
iron that tapers off at each end and is mounted on a spike
driven into a hunk of wood, so that it stands there rather
like a headless stork on one leg. It had no flat working surface
at all. In fact, it was nothing more than a man-made imita-
tion of what must have been the first 'anvil' ever used: an

irregularly shaped lump of meteoric iron which the startled finder endeavoured to beat into shape with a heavy stone.

The anvil used by the smith today, as by his predecessors for many generations past, is a very different object indeed. It is usually a 'London Pattern', or a 'Peter Wright'. It may weigh anything up to two or three hundredweight. It is made of wrought iron, and has a hardened 'blister-steel' plate welded to its flat upper surface. Its chief weight and solidity reside in its Body. This swells upwards from the base in two opposed directions, tapering off one way to a square-cut Wedge, or Hanging-end, or Heel; and the other way, through the Throat, to a cone-shaped projection of diminishing curves which bears numerous alternative names, including Beak, Bick, Beak-iron, Beak-horn or Bickern, Pike and Horn; all of them, as you can see at a glance, are pretty accurate descriptive terms.

From the blunt tip of the beak to the square-cut heel the anvil will be something over two feet in length, and perhaps six inches across. Its upper surface has been skilfully designed to serve a variety of purposes. The beak is used for curving pieces of iron, for shaping horseshoes, rings, links and shackles and so on. Next to the beak there is a smallish, square, flat area known as the Table. This has not had a blister-steel plate welded to it and is therefore softer than the rest of the anvil. It is used when iron is being cut with a cold chisel, the edge of which would be damaged if it passed right through the iron and came in contact with steel. There is a half-inch Step beyond this, leading to the Face, or main working surface. It is on this part of the anvil, extending over about two-thirds of its total length, that the bulk of the smith's heavy work is done; hence the need for a steel 'skin' to take the impact of his hammers and the weight of the forged iron itself.

Towards the end of the face, just short of the heel, there

are two holes in the anvil, each having a number of specific purposes. One of these, round and something less than an inch in diameter, is the Pritchel Hole, designed to take the round shank of a variety of tools and for receiving the point of any tool being used to punch holes into hot iron, such as the nail holes in horseshoes. The other, and larger, hole, which is square, is called the Swage Hole, or Hardie Hole. Its purpose is to take the square shanks of various Bottom Tools—cutting tools which make their impact on the under

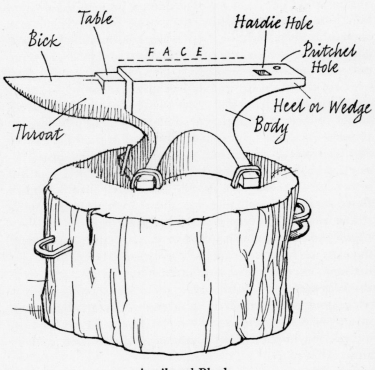

Anvil and Block

side of the work in hand when the smith strikes it from
above. Into the hardie hole, too, can be fitted the shank of
a miniature and beautifully
shaped auxiliary anvil known
as a Stake, not unlike the head
of a mountaineer's ice-pick.
The smith uses this when he
has occasion to forge something
small and delicately shaped for
which the main anvil is too
cumbersome.

Stake

The height of the anvil from
the ground is a matter of
considerable importance to the blacksmith; every bit as
important as, for instance, the height of her table or sink-
unit to the housewife. Both spend many hours of their
working days bent over these, and a few inches one way or
another can make a very great difference. The average
height of the working surface of an anvil from floor-level is
about thirty inches, or just less than that of the forge. If the
smith is a small man—and in spite of popular conception,
based perhaps on Longfellow's description, he very often is
—then he will have his anvil a few inches lower; if he is
above average height, then of course he will have it raised.

The anvil stands not on the smithy floor itself but on a
massive baulk of timber. This raises it to the requisite height
and also serves to absorb some of the shock of impact of
hammer on anvil. The baulk of timber may in fact be a
rough-hewn section of tree-trunk let three feet or so into the
brick, stone or beaten-earth floor of the smithy, with a foot
or two projecting above the floor, squared to match the base
of the anvil, which will be locked on to it by four inverted-U
clips. This, the Anvil-block, is massive, well seasoned,
slightly wider than the base of the anvil to allow for the

fixing of iron pegs and clips to hold small tools likely to be in intermittent use in the course of some specific job. Its outer face will be scored with use, the hard edges of tools, the burning fragments of metal that have spilled downwards under the hammer blows.

The position of the anvil in relation to the hearth is extremely important. For the greater part of his time the smith is occupied in transferring hot metal between forge and anvil. He does this with a swift-but-sure lateral swinging movement, passing through roughly a half-circle each way, outward and in reverse. It is essential, therefore, to have his anvil at exactly the right distance from the forge, and at the right angle to it. The beak (unless he is a left-handed smith) is always on his left side as he faces it.

This in fact is the one disadvantage of the 'rooted' anvil-block; once installed, it remains fixed permanently at the same distance from the forge. But it is obvious that if the smith is forging horseshoes he needs to be nearer than if he is forging, say, a long iron bar. So the anvil is usually set at a distance convenient for the longer (and therefore heavier) piece of work in hand. The alternative is the portable (though extremely solid) cast-iron anvil-stand. Relatively few blacksmiths, however, like using this. They maintain that it lacks the 'springiness' of the timber block which, they find, gives 'lift' to the hammer after each blow and thus enables them to strike more rapidly and at the same time with less effort. In any case, however, the anvil must be within easy reach of the forge so that the heated iron does not cool in transit; the smith must always 'strike while the iron's hot'—a familiar saying undoubtedly born in the smithy.

There is one curious aspect of the anvil that only the keen observer may spot. This is that the anvil is always set on its block so that it is pitched very slightly away from the smith, its face being therefore on a slight sideways slope. There is a reason for this. It is in order that the Scale—the loose slivers of metal that erupt from the surface of heated iron and are scattered by the hammer blows—will automatically fall clear on to the floor, thus leaving the article 'clean' when the hammering is done.

3

The smith's armoury

THE blacksmith's equipment has not changed basically in all the long centuries during which he has plied his trade. The forge; the anvil; the hammer; the tongs: these are the essential items. They were in Hephaestus's smithy, in Vulcan's smithy; in Wayland's smithy; and they are in every smithy still. An ancient engraving proves how little this equipment has changed over the years. Hephaestus's crucibles (in which he smelted his metal), his anvil, hammers of various weights and tongs of varying types, his water-trough for dowsing hot metal: all these can be matched today—except perhaps the crucibles, which belong rather to the chemist's laboratory than to the smithy.

The ring of hammer on anvil is—or used to be—one of the most characteristic sounds to be heard in the country-side. A good anvil, such as a 'Peter Wright', well mounted on its block and shrewdly struck by the smith, is capable of producing a bell-like note that can be heard on a still summer's afternoon for more than half a mile.

It is no fanciful exaggeration to state that a blacksmith's hammer is really an extension of his right hand. His hammer is the tool most constantly in his grasp. Examine a number of blacksmiths' hammers of the same apparent length and weight and you will find if you look at the handles closely that no two of them are identical. A smith must have a working hammer whose balance suits him personally. He may prefer one an inch or two longer, or shorter, than the average; he may prefer a stout haft to a slender one. In the course of years of use that haft, at the point at which he grips it, will have taken on an individuality of its own; it will, as it were, have established a personal relationship with its user. You might pick it up and not be conscious of any peculiarity; but secretly substitute another and similar hammer, and watch the expression on the blacksmith's face when he picks it up! He will know at once that he has the wrong hammer in his hand.

I am speaking at the moment of the medium-weight hand-hammer which is in constant use by the smith, not of the many others that are to be found in his armoury, kept for specific jobs. The hammer he uses most of the time is known as a Straight-peen, or Cross-peen. It weighs approximately two pounds, though some particularly muscular smiths prefer one a little heavier. It is fitted with an ash or hickory haft a foot or so in length. The steel hammer head has one very slightly convex face and one that is wedge-shaped, the angle of the wedge to the head deciding whether the hammer is straight-peen or cross-peen. Closely resembling it is another general-purpose hammer of similar weight but with a hemispherical or snub nose opposite the main striking face. This is a Ball-peen. These hammers are heavy enough for all light and medium jobs of forging, and one or other of

Ball-peen Hammer

them will rarely be out of the blacksmith's hand while he is at the anvil.

When the need arises for heavier forging—the welding of heavy-section iron bars, for instance—then the smith must call upon his apprentice, or a labourer, known in the smithy as Striker, or Hammer-man. It is he who swings the big two-handed hammers at the direction of the master smith. The implements he wields will be one or other of the heavier-weight hammers such as the Backing hammer, which weighs up to about four pounds, or the Sledge, which may weigh anything up to seven, twelve or even twenty pounds and can deliver a tremendous blow. The hafts of such hammers as these are nearly a yard long, and almost invariably made of that incomparable wood, hickory.

One of the most impressive examples of the blacksmith's technique to be seen in a smithy is the wordless collaboration between smith and striker. The striker stands on the far side of the anvil, the smith on the side nearest the hearth. The smith has his straight-peen in his right hand, while the tongs in his left hand grip the 'work' on the anvil. Neither man speaks—in words; but the smith indicates to the striker exactly where he wishes each successive blow to fall, and what type it should be, by lightly tapping the spot with his hand-hammer. The sledge, wielded by the hammer-man with both hands, falls unerringly on the spot indicated, which may change with every two or three successive blows. The alternating of the light, melodious tap-tap of the small hammer and the regular thud of the sledge sets up a rhythm which can be felt as well as heard. A knowledgeable person —another blacksmith, for instance—can tell without looking just what sort of a job is in hand; his keen ear and his own experience between them interpret the rhythm recorded on the anvil.

When the smith wishes the sledge-hammer work to come

An older rural smithy

(*Rural Industries Bureau*)

The farrier at work, with his box by his side

to a halt—perhaps because he must take a fresh heat, or because the job is completed—he still does not speak to his striker. The universal signal in blacksmithing is a light tap of the hammer on the anvil face, clear of the work. The only parallel I can think of to this device is that of the bootblack or shoeshine boy. When he has finished cleaning one shoe he rarely asks for the other foot to be placed on his block; instead, he delivers a slight, stroking blow to the wearer's shoe.

Just as the blacksmith's hand-hammer may be regarded as an extension of his own right hand, so his tongs are an extension of his left hand. The saying, 'Let not your right hand know what your left hand doeth', certainly cannot be applied to the smith. For though he does his light striking and forging with his right hand, it is the subtle movement, the sure twist and turn of left wrist and forearm, that brings the iron into position on the anvil, its strength that holds it there while he strikes it. All the time he is at his anvil the blacksmith is in fact performing complementary motions with his two hands and their basic accessories, the hammer and the tongs.

In view of the variety of jobs that a smith must undertake it is not surprising that he should equip himself with such a variety of pairs of tongs. Their number greatly exceeds even the widest range of hammers a smith uses—a number in fact considerably greater than the few mentioned already, and often forged by the smith himself out of a discarded half-axle from some derelict car, to serve some specific purpose. He may have a dozen hammers in use, large and small; but he will have three or four times that number of pairs of tongs, no two pairs of them alike. Most if not all of them he will almost certainly have designed and forged for himself.

In a Kentish smithy I know well there is an iron rail running the whole length of one wall beside the forge.

D

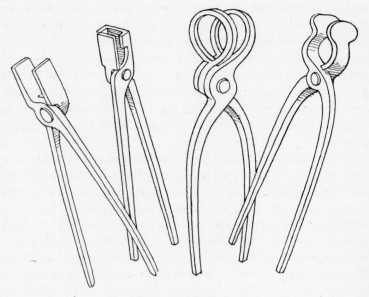

Blacksmiths' Tongs

Hanging over it there are more pairs of smiths' tongs than I could easily count, and no two pairs of them identical. The smith there has made every one of them. At least, his father before him made the majority of them, used them throughout his own long working life, and handed them on to his son nearly twenty years ago when he came out of the army and took over the smithy. At first sight there seems little if anything to choose among most of them, except that some appear to have straight jaws while others have jaws set at an angle. But a closer look soon dispels that illusion.

These tongs were all designed and forged for specific jobs. They have been given the shape and dimensions that have been found most suitable by many generations of smiths, all

of whom have taken pride in forging their own tools. They
bear names such as Half-round, Wide, Close, Flat, Square,
Round, Three-side, and so on. Some have jaws that give a
flat, parallel grip; others take a firm grip on a round bar of,
say, three-quarter-inch diameter; yet others are designed to
grip square-section bars diagonally, for increased rigidity;
others again are for hexagonal bars or half-round. Some are
fashioned bulb-shaped, so that while the extremities of the
jaws will grip the iron, the curved parts will clear a collar or
some other projection. Others consist of two matching jaws,
one 'male' the other 'female', so shaped that one fits into
the other, effectively gripping a small-section piece of iron
that requires particularly delicate manipulation. There are
right-angle tongs for holding ironwork in a certain position
for forging on the anvil. In fact, the variety is almost infinite.
And, like so many objects designed for a specific purpose,
they have an intrinsic and characteristic individual beauty;
some of them are like buds about to open, others like flowers
in bloom, others again like exotic sea-shells.

All, however, have one thing in common: the handles, or
Reins, as the smith refers to them, are approximately twenty
inches long from the pivot of the jaws, while the jaws themselves will be only about three or four inches long at the
most, and often only an inch or two. Such a ratio of reins to
jaws has been found to give the most effective leverage and
grip. Reins are usually of round or square section, less than
half an inch in thickness, and close to parallel when they are
being used. This means that the smith does not have to open
his hand unduly wide while gripping them. To save himself
effort on a long sustained job, or when he is doing swift
repetition work in stages, he will often slip over the ends of
the reins an iron loop that exactly grips them under tension.
He knows then that the iron he is working will be securely
held by the jaws when he momentarily lays down his tongs

in the fire to take a fresh heat while he turns his attention to something else.

Though a selection of tongs likely to be required for any job immediately in hand may be kept not on the rail but upside down in the bosh, the smith knows at a glance exactly which pair he is picking up, even though its jaws are invisible; indeed, he may not even need to look at them: his fingers will tell him whether or not he has the right pair the instant they close about the reins. If he is having to return his work to the fire-pit to take frequent fresh heats his tongs soon become very hot, so at intervals he drops them back into the water to quench. The hiss they make at such times is a characteristic feature of any smithy.

Hard, tough and heavy-handed as he may seem, no craftsman is more careful about the use and maintenance of his tools than the blacksmith. Perhaps this is in part because, unlike any other craftsman you could name, he has himself designed and forged the tools of his trade; therefore they have a particular importance to him, a sort of personal relationship. One of the first tasks an apprentice blacksmith has to undertake is the designing and forging of a few assorted pairs of tongs for his own use. He makes them under the eye of the master smith. He may at first be content with them, but it is probable that he will soon discard them, for they will lack the quality of good workmanship that would be found in tongs made by an expert. After a while he will be on his way to becoming an expert, and he will replace those immature tongs by tongs forged with the greater skill he has acquired.

*   *   *   *

A smith's hammers and tongs are his basic tools, in continuous, everyday use throughout his working life. It should not be supposed, however, that the hammers range simply from the two-pound hand-hammer to the twenty-pound sledge. Far from it. Look around any smithy and you will find an extraordinary array of hammers which are variants of the basic type, even though they are not immediately recognizable as such.

For example, there will be a wide range of Hot Sets and Cold Sets. These are a type of hammer used by the master smith for cutting metal while his striker wields the sledge. They have a variety of edges, sharpish or blunt according to whether they are to cut hot or cold metal. Very occasionally they are fitted with a wooden haft; but far more often the haft consists of a length of thin rod or a hazel or withy bent round a 'waist' in the head and gripped like the reins of a pair of tongs. There is a reason for fitting this curious type of handle: the impact of a heavy sledge on the top face of the set can jar the holder very severely indeed if he is gripping anything as rigid as a wooden haft, so the blacksmith avoids this by adopting a simple and at the same time very effective device.

Another type of hammer has a wide, flat, square head and is known as a Flatter, or Flattener—a name which adequately describes its purpose. It is used for restoring the surface of a piece of iron that has been misshapen in the process of forging. Alongside the row of flatters there may be a row of hammers even more odd in appearance, known as Fullers. These will be of varying sizes, the larger ones designed to be used in conjunction with the sledge, while the smaller ones can be held by the smith in his left hand while he strikes with his hand-hammer. The striking faces of these fullers, instead of being large and square and flat, will be shaped in a variety of convex curves, as they are designed for the forming of channels or grooves of various sections in heated iron. Used in this way, they become Top or Bottom Tools.

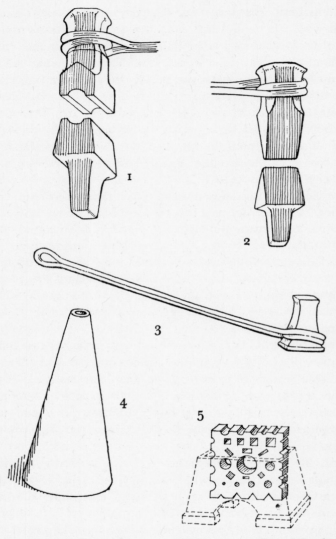

1: Swages   2: Fullers   3: Flatter   4: Floor Mandrel
5: Swage-block and Stand

As top tools, they are laid over the work in hand and struck with the sledge. But each top tool has a matching bottom tool, fitted with a short stem which can be inserted in the hardie hole. The iron is then laid upon this and hammered direct with the sledge. Or, if the shape is to be given to both sides of the iron, matching fullers, top and bottom, are used, and the sledge applied as before. Thus the groove or channel or indentation can be formed in the iron on one or other or both sides at once. A well-equipped smithy has a whole battery of these top and bottom tools to serve every need that arises.

The surest method of reducing a piece of wrought iron or mild steel to the shape required, when it is other than flat or square, is to use the Swage-block or a suitable Swage. This is the method usually adopted when repetition work is in hand. The swage-block is a massive lump of cast-iron or steel, roughly rectangular overall but indented and pierced with a great number of varied slots, holes and grooves of different radius, half-round and V-shaped channels of different depths and angles, and so on. It usually lies on the floor in some corner where no one will trip over it, but when the smith requires to use it he will mount it on a framework of its own, designed to hold it rigid in any one of its six possible positions. It is substantial enough for him to be able to place a piece of heated iron in any one of its slots, grooves or angles and hammer it into the required shape; in fact it is an auxiliary anvil.

For lighter work, however, the smith may prefer to use any one of his stock of swages, each one of which will be shaped like one or other of the indentations in the swage-block. The swages are handier to use; they can be used as top or bottom tools, or both. Top swages resemble hammers, while bottom swages are dropped into the hardie hole, like the less elaborate fullers.

Like the fullers, swages are kept in matching pairs, and the smith will see to it that they are hung or stacked in pairs, so that there will be no risk of using two swages of differing section unless this unusual treatment is actually called for by the type of work in hand. So frequently are these particular tools in use that the square hole in the heel of the anvil is known as often as a swage hole as a hardie hole. The swage-block may be regarded as a sort of cast-iron 'omnibus' tool, offering an immense variety of 'moulds' in which heated iron can be hammered to shape; the individual swages have each their particular characteristic size, shape, contour and depth, and are of course handier to use on individual jobs at anvil height.

No smithy is ever without a curious-looking object that, like the swage-block, stands on the floor, out of the way of people coming and going but handy for use when required. In appearance it resembles the traditional Welshwoman's hat, or witch's hat; it is a hollow cone of cast-iron standing about three feet high, perhaps a foot across at the base and tapering to an inch or two at the top. This is a Floor Mandrel, and its purpose is not hard to guess.

Cone-shaped and perfectly circular, it can be used for truing-up any hoop or ring or iron tyre that the smith has rough-forged, from a foot in diameter down to a few inches. It is less often called into use nowadays than it was some years ago, for the trolleys, trucks and barrows that were formerly fitted with iron-bound wheels now usually have rubber tyres. Of one thing, however, the blacksmith can be pretty sure: if he were to discard the mandrel on the grounds that it occupied valuable space, need would quite certainly arise before very long.

Even now we have come nowhere near the full tally of tools large and small that form the smith's armoury. If hammers and tongs and sets and swages come high up among essentials they are closely followed by a bewildering variety of smaller tools.

These include Cold Chisels, Punches, Drifts, Bolsters, Hardies, Jigs, Hand-mandrels, Scroll-dogs, Scroll-forms, Calipers, Dividers, Files, Brass Rule (an iron or steel one would be useless in a smithy for frequent contact with hot metal and water would soon cause it to corrode) and a variety of Monkey-tools. They may be kept on shelves handy for immediate use; they may be clipped into panels over the rugged bench that usually runs along one wall of the smithy beneath its largest window and carries the vices, hand or machine drills and other standing equipment; or they may simply be lumped together in some massive wooden chest, to be drawn out from beneath the bench when the need arises. But somewhere or other they exist; and they are in frequent if intermittent use.

The purpose of many of them is obvious at a glance. Those heavy chisels, for instance—so different from the slim blades of the cabinet-maker's chisels with their smooth boxwood handles—with wedge-shaped cutting edges: they are obviously for shearing metal under the weight of a heavy hammer. The punches, too, are obviously for driving holes of varying shapes and sizes into metal of varying thickness. They may be square, round, hexagonal, rectangular, triangular; they will taper smoothly towards one end and have a solid cap at the other, with its edge burred over from the impact of the hammer. These tools are used over the anvil's pritchel hole, or over a hole in the swage-block, so that the point emerges from the iron without coming into contact with metal hard enough to blunt it.

Drifts at first glance resemble punches, and like the punches are almost always made by the smith for his own use. In general they are slightly larger, for their purpose is to enlarge a hole already punched into hot iron and in so

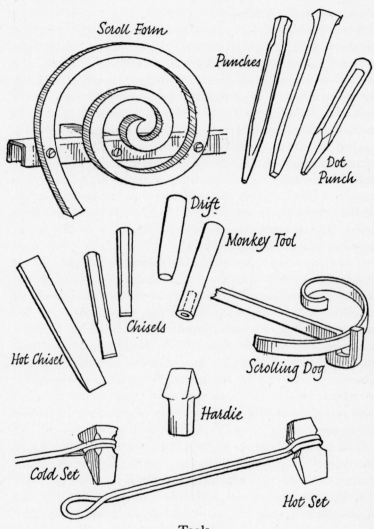

Scroll Form

Punches

Dot Punch

Drift

Monkey Tool

Hot Chisel

Chisels

Scrolling Dog

Hardie

Cold Set

Hot Set

Tools

doing to smooth the interior surface, whatever its punched-out shape may be. For this reason drifts are usually more accurately shaped, their taper more gradual, their section more exact. Whereas the punch is generally driven straight through from one side of the iron to the other, the corresponding drift will be driven in, a stage at a time, first from one side and then from the other. With these tools, as with the punches, the smith invariably works over pritchel. or hardie hole or a recess in the swage-block.

The list of a blacksmith's tools appears limitless; he accumulates about him an ever-increasing variety of items large and small, rarely throwing anything away unless it is damaged absolutely beyond repair. Even then it is often possible to fashion a smaller tool out of part of the broken larger one: the smith is a born improviser. Many of his tools, his hammers, tongs, punches, drifts, chisels, swages and sets, are in almost continual use; others lie on shelves or dangle over rails within handy reach, fill the heavy sliding drawers beneath the bench or lie scattered about on the bench itself, where the 'cold work' is carried out. To the untutored eye there may not seem much law and order, rhyme and reason, about the deployment of the tools, but if you watch a smith at work you will notice that he is never at a loss as to where to lay his hand on just that tool he needs for some specific job, however brief and temporary. His hand reaches out, and the tool seems to appear as by magic within his grasp.

Cold work is the work he does on iron that he has already forged hot and permitted to cool. It is bench work: mainly drilling and filing, with a little light hammering and adjustment such as the material can take 'cold' without risk of damage or weakening. A blacksmith's bench bears little resemblance to that of a joiner. Whereas the joiner's bench is long and low, with a recessed surface running the full

length to take the shavings and sawdust and thus give him
an overall level surface to work on, and still showing the
grain of the timber of which it was made, the blacksmith's
bench, from sustained contact with iron, grease, heat, heavy
tools and so on, looks not unlike a slab of iron itself.

It must, of course, be immensely sturdy, for it has to
withstand strains very much greater than those to which a
joiner subjects his bench. Its timbers may be three or four
inches or more thick, clamped together at the corners with
iron straps. It may be mounted on heavy baulks of timber,
or bolted down (with deeply countersunk bolts to avoid
damage to tools) to a heavy-gauge iron framework. It hardly
looks like wood at all. It is grey-black from years of contact
with metal in the process of being drilled, filed and otherwise treated cold. It is greasy to the touch, the result of years
of spilled oil mixed with fine iron-filings from drills and other
bench tools, and scarred where heavy metal objects have
been dropped on it.

The well-equipped bench has
two vices on its near edge, one
towards each end. One of
the vices will be of the standard engineer's pattern, strong
enough for all ordinary jobs
such as filing and finishing. The
other will be what is known as
a Leg-vice. This is a bigger
affair altogether, with massive
four- or six-inch jaws. Because
it is intended to stand up to an
indefinite amount of bending,
screwing-round, shearing and
twisting with powerful two-
handed wrenches, it is fitted

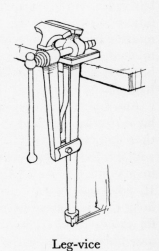

Leg-vice

with a long 'leg' driven deep into the smithy floor immediately beneath it and anchored there either in stone or brick or a metal plate. It locks bench to floor, and is integral with both.

Its jaws are massive enough for it to serve as a bench anvil. The smith may use it instead of his main anvil when he wants to hammer a piece of iron into a true right angle—when, for example, he is making a set of medium-sized wall-brackets. He may use it to hold his scroll-form, rather than drop this into the hardie hole of his anvil and be obliged to bend low over it.

Both vices, of course, are made of cast steel or they could never stand up to the brutal treatment they will inevitably receive throughout the whole of their lifetimes. They are virtually indestructible—like the anvil and the swage-block. Though scarred, they gleam with regular use. Examining the leg-vice in a smithy recently I found that the three-quarter-inch hole through which the twin-knobbed tommy-bar slides to tighten or loosen the jaws has been worn from full round to elliptical, so long has it been in use. It is a massive bar, that slides in a massive bearing. When it slides to a stop after the smith has screwed up the vice it makes a bell-like note comparable with that of the smith's hand-hammer on his anvil.

Another fixture always to be found on the bench is the hand-operated or power-operated vertical drill. More often than not, even today, it is the hand-operated version that you will see, for the smith believes that he can work to within finer limits when he controls the wheel with his own hands. If, however, he happens to have some scores of identical holes to drill—as in the main frame of a wrought-iron gate, for example, where innumerable rivets have to be inserted and hammered home—he may prefer the power-operated drill: it is, after all, repetition work that he will have in hand.

But for odd drilling jobs, and invariably for the larger holes, he will almost certainly prefer to operate his drill by hand. That same West Country smith who prefers the traditional type of bellows to the more modern fan has put it on record that in his smithy all holes larger than a quarter of an inch diameter are drilled by hand. It is small points such as these that characterize the smith who is artist as well as craftsman.

*   *   *   *

So much for an outline of the blacksmith's main and secondary equipment, from forge, anvil and bellows by way of hammer and tongs down to punches, drifts and drills. But if these were all, then the smithy would appear an empty, unused place indeed: a display of tools and miscellaneous gear, but little else. However, this is far from being the case. For the smithies still to be found up and down the country—in Sussex and Kent, in Wessex and Wales, in Derbyshire and Lancashire, Yorkshire and Durham, in the Lake District and East Anglia and elsewhere—have much more than this to show (see plate opposite page 48).

They have what is perhaps best of all: their work-in-progress, evidence that they are alive, not just museum-pieces evoking an age that is past. Spades and shovels await the fitting of new hafts, the tightening of worn rivets. Shears large and small await grinding and setting. There is a pile of newly forged harrow tines, threaded to fit that harrow propped against the wall outside the smithy, waiting to be screwed and locked in position. There is an old-fashioned cottage fender, of punched iron and brass, awaiting a job of welding and brazing, and with it a heavy iron coal-scuttle whose bottom has cracked and now requires expert patching.

There is a car's luggage-grid with a fractured angle-piece

that must be welded when the smith can get around to it. There is an old-style barrow wheel whose tyre has worked loose as the felloes shrank in the heat of the sun so that the tyre must be reduced in size and shrunk on again to bind them tight. Near it is a pair of broken gate hinges to be matched and replaced if they cannot be repaired, and alongside them the rusted bracket of the village inn-sign, likewise corroded by the weather and needing an extra bar to reinforce it so that it can suspend the sign for another century or so. There are two sets of horseshoes, lying in a corner waiting to be fitted to that mare whose owner promised to bring her in several days ago, and the draught horse the smith knows to be overdue for its new set.

Standing against the wall there is a set of car springs, one leaf of which has 'gone', so that the whole must be dismantled and a new leaf made, tempered and fitted. It belongs to that ancient car standing in the smithy yard with one axle jacked up on a stout and grimy wooden chest. Leaning against the bench is a tractor tow-bar whose swivel-joint has snapped and now awaits repair, for its owner is anxious to get on with a haulage job on his farm. On the bench itself there lies a length of heavy chain with one broken link; until a new link of the same gauge and toughness has been forged the chain is useless. One more urgent job for the busy smith.

Like the list of his tools and gear, the oddments on the smithy floor are too many to count. They are the property of half a hundred customers in the district—some of them perhaps from many miles away. They are the clear evidence of the vital part the smith plays in the communal life of the district in which his smithy is a focal point—as it may well have been for many centuries past.

4

Forging the shoe

UNTIL comparatively recently in the centuries-old history of blacksmithery the sign outside a smithy usually read: 'Shoeing and General Smith'. But those smithies are decreasing in number every year. Of those that remain, those in which the smith still has enough work to keep him busy throughout his working week, most are now concerned almost solely with the repair and maintenance of agricultural machinery. The smith has probably painted out the word 'Shoeing'. Now and then you will come across a smithy whose owner is grimly hanging on to the past. I know of one such in an East Sussex village. There is a notice permanently pinned to the smithy door, reading: 'If Smith Required Please Apply At Cottage'. An arrow points to the cottage next door. The probability is that the smith is cultivating his vegetable garden. I have been past that smithy many times in the last year or two, and only once or twice heard the sweet music of his hammer on the anvil and seen smoke rising from the forge chimney.

That particular smith's misfortune is that he does not happen to be in a district containing riding-schools and hunting- or racing-stables. If these were abundant he would have all the work he could handle, and would certainly give pride of place in the sign above his door to that initial word 'Shoeing'. He would be a full-time shoesmith, or farrier, like the smith I know so well on the Kent-Sussex border whose time is fully occupied six days a week—and, quite often, he has told me, on Sunday mornings too. Six days a week he shoes horses in his smithy from daybreak to midday; and in the afternoons he takes a light portable anvil and a kit of basic tools and visits his clients in all directions within a radius of fifteen miles or so, to 'cold-shoe' their horses on the spot. More than half his shoeing is, in fact, done in this way. No fewer than four hundred horses, he told me, form his clientele and depend on him for his services. There cannot be many farriers in the country today who are still as busy as he is.

He claims—and I am sure from what I know of him that this is no idle boast—that he knows every individual in his clientele 'by heart'. Before now, I have picked up from a pile of ready-forged shoes lying on the smithy floor, usually clipped together in fours with a piece of wire, a set which to my untutored eye looked exactly the same as any other of a dozen odd sets. They all had their clips in the same position; all had the four narrow rectangular holes on the outer curve and three on the inner curve, cut deep in the narrow groove that runs round the periphery of the shoe on the under side. His quick eye takes note. There may or may not be a twinkle in it as he quietly names the horse for which the set of shoes had been made, adding its owner's name and address, as though I might want to verify the accuracy of his memory.

His memory. Once he has measured a horse's hoof and made and fitted a set of shoes, those measurements, together with any individual characteristics, are, as it were, photographically imprinted upon it. The owner may ring him up and say that such and such a horse has cast a shoe; can he please come over and fit another? The smith identifies the horse concerned by a swift glance through his mental index file, picks out a shoe if he has made one already against just such an emergency, or quickly forges one to the measurements he carries in that astonishing memory of his. That

E

afternoon he will be out at the farm or stables with his mobile outfit and the cast shoe will have been replaced in a matter of minutes.

The shoeing smith is the modern representative of an ancient and honourable tradition. Strictly speaking he should be referred to—as he still is in the cavalry and mounted police—as a farrier. The very name suggests its antiquity for the word comes from the Latin word for iron: *ferrum*. So far as we know, the Romans, though they made use of horses, did not have them iron-shod. This cannot be absolutely proved, for iron is a metal that disintegrates rapidly; rust, oxydization, sets in and eventually the object of which it was made becomes unrecognizable. Certainly no horseshoes have been discovered that are indisputably of Roman origin.

Some very ancient horseshoes, however, have occasionally come to light: shoes that can be fairly positively dubbed 'Romano-British'—that is to say they date from the period of Roman occupation in the early years of the Christian era. There are Celtic horseshoes, too, and Saxon ones; but these are almost as rare as the Romano-British, and are cherished in museums in hermetically sealed cases, individually treated with special anti-oxydization preservatives as though they were as precious as gold.

These rare specimens reveal how the horseshoe has evolved from the earliest clumsy examples to the beautifully designed shoe of the hunter and race-horse today. Examination of the shoes throws a good deal of light not merely on the skill but on the resources available to the smith of those distant days. For example, the earliest-known horseshoes, instead of having the familiar smooth outer and inner curves which we find in shoes today, presented an outline consisting of a series of six or more wavy bulges between point and point. The bulges were the result of the punching of nail holes; the smith

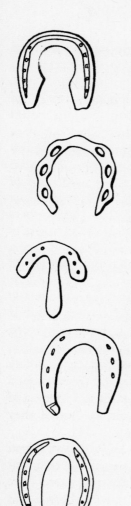

had not the knowledge necessary to eliminate the bulges without compressing the holes and thus rendering them useless. The nail holes, too, were much larger than the holes used today; instead of being narrow, countersunk slots they were either round or oval, to take a round-capped or 'domed' nail, a nail so massive that it must often have damaged the hoof into which it was driven. The horse walked on these domes, not on the shoe itself.

These very early shoes had other characteristics which can be interpreted today by the expert. They were apparently shaped from a forged bar not more than half an inch or so wide, and fairly thin; the shoes when new, it has been calculated, probably weighed less than half a pound apiece. This contrasts with a working horse's shoe of later date which, in the case of a heavy draught horse such as the brewers use to haul their drays, could

Some old horseshoes. Compare them with the modern shoe in the bottom left-hand corner

weigh anything up to two or even three pounds apiece. The early shoes, like today's, would be smooth and flat on the face that is in contact with the hoof; but the working face was usually convex—again in contrast to the later and the modern shoe.

Over succeeding centuries the design of the shoe changed a good deal from the early prototype. The irregular wavy bulges disappeared altogether: evidence that the smith had learned how to punch holes without distorting the iron, or to reshape the iron without compressing the holes. The shape of these changed from round or oval to narrow and rectangular, and were countersunk so that the shoe itself, not just the nail heads, made contact with the ground. The number of nail holes increased from six to eight, or even ten; where the number was an odd one the extra hole was always placed in the shoe's outer edge, as it still is today.

It is not difficult to deduce why these changes came about. It must have become obvious that the wear and tear on a few domed nail heads was necessarily more rapid than it would be on an unbroken, uniform surface or iron. Hence the advent of flat-topped nails, countersunk to protect their heads, such as are almost universally used today. The old-style dome-headed nails, however, had one outstanding merit: they gave the horse a grip on a smooth surface. So, the smith's ingenuity was called upon to find a compromise. The result was the forging of what are called Calkins; these are blunt, downturned ends to the heel of each shoe, cut off square so as to give a substantial 'bite'. They are most commonly found on the shoes of heavy draught horses, particularly in areas where they have to work over cobblestones or wet, smooth and greasy roads. The calkins enormously increase the grip of the shoe on any hard but slippery surface.

Now the under side of the shoe had calkins to render the grip more efficient, but there still remained the problem of

A detail of the hinge work on the slype door from St Albans Abbey.
Twelfth century

Part of the Eleanor Grille in Westminster Abbey, by Thomas de Leghtone. 1294

(Dean and Chapter of Westminster Abbey)

the worn nail head. It was some centuries before the smith evolved the practice of 'fullering' the under side of the horseshoe. This meant using his fuller to cut a groove right round the inside of the periphery; in this indentation he punched his narrow nail holes, and thus preserved the life of the nail and that of the shoe longer than had ever been possible before. This use of the fullered groove is matched exactly by the shoemaker, who cuts a diagonal slit all round the sole, just inside its periphery, to take his row of stitches; the leather then closes down upon the stitching and the waxed thread is preserved against abrasion until the leather itself is worn down to the base of the slit.

The blacksmith was always an experimentalist, and many of the horseshoes that have been salvaged and preserved for examination show the lengths to which he went. There was a period when he used to forge what, because of its odd shape, is now known as the 'keyhole' shoe. It appeared as early as Shakespeare's day—four centuries ago—and was popular for many generations onwards. This shoe was broader than its predecessors and thus provided a larger surface for contact with the ground, which in those days was equally soft whether it was road or field, except in times of frost or drought. It was characterized by an almost circular hollow in the forward part, to take the 'frog' of the hoof, and broadened out behind this, tapering away to a wedge-shaped heel. It had as many as ten nail holes, all countersunk in a fullered groove.

A variant of this was the 'tongue' shoe. In this type the inner side was almost straight for the greater part of its length, affording even better contact with the ground but adding not a little to the overall weight. Romano-British horseshoes may have weighed less than half a pound; these medieval and later shoes weighed six, seven, even eight times as much. Their other disadvantage was that though they might be excellent on a hard, dry surface, as soon as the horse went on to soft, spongy ground the suction caused by the expanse of smooth metal added enormously to the strain of lifting the hoof and all too frequently resulted not only in the loss of the shoe but in damage to the foot as the nails were dragged out of it.

Gradually, however, the horseshoe, through a long period of trial and error, came to assume the shape most familiar to us today: a shapely curve with a triangular clip midway along its periphery. It is actually a century and a half since a farrier made the first 'clip' shoe. He forged a small triangular projection, or 'lug', that pointed upwards and sloped very slightly backwards from the toe. The clip served—and it still serves, for the smith found it good and retained the pattern— a twofold purpose: it not only gives extra grip on the hoof to augment that of the nails, but when the shoe is being fitted it enables the smith to fix the shoe in exactly the right position for the driving in of the nails.

An alternative device, the invention of a veterinary surgeon, was the 'upturn' shoe. In this shoe the whole of the toe was curved upwards and back over the front of the hoof. It did not prove as popular as the other type, however, and for two reasons: it called for much more elaborate forging and it added considerably to the weight. Nor was the roll-over, or up-turn, any more efficient than the clip. Certain owners continued to demand this type of shoe, nevertheless, giving as their reason the fact that the curve nicely matched the circular motion, or roll, of the horse's foot in leaving and returning to the ground. A slow-motion film shows that this so-called 'roll' is in fact a feature of the movement, accentuated in certain classes of horse and at certain rates of travel.

In medieval times a smith's charge for making a single shoe was about one farthing—a penny for a set of four. This, even allowing for the substantial increase in the value of money over the centuries, seems an extremely modest charge. Today the farrier charges according to the type of shoe, its weight and size, and his price will range between twenty shillings for a set of small shoes and thirty shillings or more for a large and heavy set. If he is called upon to make a special set, whether for hunting or racing or for a horse with some malformation in one or more of its hooves, then naturally he makes a higher charge still.

Once the fullered shoe—that is, the shoe with the curved groove in which the nail heads lie countersunk—became the standard type, the smith found that he had to expend a great deal of time and effort fullering the iron bars from which he worked. It was heavy, tedious, unrewarding work. In time, however, the foundries that supplied the raw material of the blacksmith's trade began to turn out ready-fullered mild-steel bars, so that much of the tedious labour and unprofitable time in the smithy was saved.

Nowadays the bars usually come in eighteen-foot lengths, under the general term Concave Bars. They are graded according to their section. For small shoes the smith will use, for example, $\frac{1}{2}$ in. by $\frac{1}{4}$ in., or $\frac{5}{8}$ in. by $\frac{1}{4}$ in. concave. For rather heavier shoes he will take $\frac{3}{4}$ in. by $\frac{1}{2}$ in., or $\frac{7}{8}$ in. by $\frac{1}{2}$ in. For heavy cart-horse shoes the measurements will rise proportionately to about $1\frac{1}{8}$ in. or $1\frac{1}{4}$ in. by $\frac{1}{2}$ in. or $\frac{3}{4}$ in.; but in the case of these extra-heavy shoes the bar will be plain, not fullered, the nails being individually countersunk below the overall surface. A fullered shoe would pick up far too much heavy soil when the horse was, for example, working on ploughland.

*   *   *   *

The first step in the making of a set of shoes is to snip off —either with a powerful pair of mechanical shears or by cutting on the anvil with chisel or set—the appropriate length of the selected bar. The farrier has a convenient rule-of-thumb method of gauging the length to be cut. He has of course first taken the measurement of the hooves to be shod. He does this in the smithy if the horse is one that he has not shod before, though if it is one of his 'regulars' its measurements are already stored in that extraordinarily retentive memory of his.

He takes the measurement across the broadest part of the hoof. Hind hooves are generally about a quarter of an inch wider than fore hooves, and he therefore cuts his bars to match. His rule-of-thumb is simple: twice the width of the hoof at its maximum point, plus two inches for a heavy horse or one inch for a lighter horse. The ratio given is never far from exact, but he can always snip off the surplus metal from the heel of the shoe when finishing it off if he finds that he has overestimated it. (He is careful never to underestimate, for this would involve making a 'short' shoe, or lengthening it by reducing its section.)

Having cut off the length required—say, for example, a fourteen-inch length, suitable for a horse whose hoof is six inches across at the widest part—he then cuts a similar length for the matching hoof, and another pair for the other hooves, somewhat shorter if they are for the fore feet, longer if for the hind feet. If the owner is in a hurry, then the smith will proceed to forge all four shoes at the same time, though this involves extremely hard and concentrated effort. He really prefers to forge them in pairs. As you watch him at work you will come to realize how great a demand even this makes upon his skill, endurance and concentration, and at the same time how economical a deployment of his strength and tools this method demonstrates.

For to forge two shoes at the same time means keeping each length of iron in the fire-pit at exactly the right temperature and in exactly the right position, while he works at his anvil on the other of the pair. (If he is forging four shoes at a time this becomes even more exacting.) The process in any case is one of rotation, with each shoe one stage behind the other throughout, from start to finish. This idea may be easier to grasp if we take the process of making a shoe stage by stage. Incidentally, it may well be that this practice in the smithy gave birth to the familiar phrase, 'To have more than one iron in the fire'.

Having picked up the first bar—a fourteen-inch length, let us say, of $\frac{3}{4}$ in. by $\frac{1}{2}$ in. concave—he thrusts it into his heat and watches it begin to glow. When it has reached exactly the right temperature he seizes it with the appropriate pair of tongs in his left hand, whips it out and drops it on to the anvil. It is red-hot for rather more than half its length, the tongs gripping it by the cooler end. In the hardie hole is his Heel-cropper. This is a bottom tool so shaped that when the hot end of a bar is laid on it and struck by the hammer it is nicely rounded off. The process is known as 'rounding the heel' and is used only in the case of light- and medium-weight shoes, to give them a nice finish. On heavier shoes there will probably be calkins, and therefore the ends must be kept blunt.

The bar is then laid across the far edge of the anvil face and struck two or three times with the hand-hammer. These blows bend the bar to approximately the curve of a boomerang, a 'soft angle' of, say, 135 degrees or so. By now, however, it has almost ceased to glow, so it is slipped back into the fire-pit and the second bar, which has now reached the correct glowing temperature, is whipped out to receive the same treatment: two, three or four shrewd blows, and the bar has assumed a curved angle identical with that of the first. Back in the fire-pit they resemble a pair of well-matched boomerangs taking a fresh heat before undergoing the next process.

Now the initial bar comes out again. This time it is dropped on to the anvil face with the hot end downwards and the cool end upwards. The smith strikes it smartly and the angle-curve partially closes, the two heels of the shoe curving towards each other and the near-straight edges taking on at last the unmistakable curve that will eventually match the curve of the horse's hoof.

By this time, however, the curved bar has acquired something of a twist, and this must now be eliminated. The smith lays it on the anvil face and strikes it a firm blow, perhaps two, at exactly the right spot. With deft movements of his supple and powerful wrist, communicated down the reins of his tongs, he works the shoe this way and that, and with a succession of hammer blows, all delivered at exactly the right speed and weight, he trues up the shoe before it has cooled down too much for further working.

The second shoe takes its place on the anvil, to go through the same process. There is a rhythmic swing between forge and anvil as the smith exchanges shoe for shoe in the successive stages of forging. This rhythm is never hurried, never leisurely, but somewhere between the two. Anyone who has watched a countryman at work—swinging a scythe, perhaps, or loading sheaves of corn on to a waggon or a rick—will have recognized that though he appears to work leisurely and without hurrying, in fact he gets through an astonishing amount of work in a given time. The secret lies largely in the rhythm which he has found to be most natural to him, and which he automatically maintains throughout his working hours. It is exactly the same with the blacksmith. You will rarely see him hurry; equally, you will rarely find him idling.

The shoe is now taking on its final shape, to within a few hammer blows one way or the other. Having bent the bar first over the far edge of the anvil and then downwards upon the face, he then transfers it to the beak, on which, holding it firmly with his tongs, he hammers it to the exact curve required. The convex curve of the beak smooths and rounds-out the inner curve of the shoe, and the outer curve follows this as a result of the continual hammering the smith maintains as he moves it along the curve of the beak. From time to time he thrusts the shoe back into the fire to take another heat, meanwhile taking out the next shoe for the same treatment on the anvil.

And now it is ready for punching. It has been deep in the fire-pit and emerged red-hot all over from toe to heel. He lays it on the anvil, and then drops his tongs into the bosh to quench until they are required again. Next he picks up a punch, sometimes known as a Stamp. It is flat in the grip and its lower end is tapered off, rectangular in section, to a blunt point. In fact, what he is now holding is a hand-made punch —hand-made from the 'tang' of an outworn and discarded file which he has forged and retempered to remove its brittleness and which has now just the right degree of hard-ness and toughness for its new use.

Briskly, but without hurry, he drops the tapered end into the groove of the shoe and punches a succession of holes— two, three, four—round the curve, until the iron has cooled too much to take any more from the punch. He whips the shoe back into the fire, extracts its fellow and gives it the same treatment. Out again, and he completes the tally of holes in the first shoe; out yet again, and he completes the punching of the second shoe. Had it been a small shoe there would be no more than three holes on each side of the centre of the toe—where the clip has yet to be forged. On a larger shoe there will be an uneven number of holes, with the extra nail always on the outer curve.

The first punching of the nail holes goes only part-way through the iron; it is, in fact, little more than a starter, or a guide. Now the smith takes up another and somewhat larger punch, known as a Pritchel. Like the stamp, it is hand-made from an old rasp, slightly bigger in section than the file and designed to give the exact rectangular proportions of the final nail hole.

Because the pritchel will pierce right through the iron he works now over the pritchel hole, into which the blunt point will protrude a quarter of an inch or so. He is actually holding the shoe with the pritchel while he works, having no further use for his tongs at this stage. The lower edge of his hand is within a few inches of the red-hot metal. But he has long been inured to such heat. He is more concerned for his pritchel and the effect of the hot iron on its temper. You will notice that between each set of holes and the next, and sometimes between hole and hole, he quenches the tool for a moment. The faint repeated hiss from the dark water in the bosh at his elbow is one of the characteristic sounds of a smithy when horseshoes are being forged: it is brief and reiterated, as though a small snake were registering hostility in the darkness.

The shoe is almost, but not quite, completed. The smith turns it over and chips away the little 'wire-edge' of metal that his pritchel lifted as it emerged. If necessary he inserts it again, this time from the reverse side, and very slightly enlarges the rectangle. Usually, however, the weight of his hammer and his sureness of touch have been sufficient in themselves to give the hole the required dimensions without this extra trimming.

The shoe now goes back into the fire again: he has still to make the clip, before giving the final touches to the shoe and leaving it to cool in readiness for fitting. The forging of the clip is perhaps the most delicate operation of all.

Hitherto he has been using a light hammer—unless he has been working on a particularly heavy set of shoes. This will

The gates of Chirk Castle, near Llangollen, by the Davies brothers. 1719

(Lieutenant-Colonel R. Myddelton)

A gate at New College, Oxford, by Thomas Robinson. 1711

have been his cross-peen or straight-peen. He may continue to use this handy all-purpose hammer even for making his clips, but he is more likely to lay it aside and pick up the oddest-looking hammer in all his armoury of these essential tools. This is his Cat's-head. It has a heavy head, with two main striking faces on opposite sides of the hickory haft, and two small, wedge-shaped projections opposite each other and at right angles to the main faces. These somewhat resemble a pair of ears—hence, perhaps, the term 'cat's-head'; or it may simply be the squareness of the head that has something in common with the head of a cat. It is, in fact, a four-face hammer, though two of the faces are little more than small, blunt wedges. It is these that he calls into use when forging his clips.

This clip is a triangular, tapering 'lug', sometimes referred to as a 'web', that is extruded by hammering from the curved iron of the shoe, either in the centre of the toe or (if it is a large shoe, with two clips) one on each side of the central point.

To make it, the smith lays his shoe, red-hot at the exact point, on the far edge of the anvil and strikes it sharply with the wedge face of his cat's-head. First there is a slight recess, or dent, in the edge of the iron; repeated and accurate striking with the hammer forces the soft metal outwards and upwards in such a way that it automatically assumes the hollow triangular shape of a cat's ear. Blunt at the base, where it 'grows' out of the iron, it tapers off to a fine edge at the point, and is in fact about as sharp as a bluntish knife-point. To watch this process, so swift and sure, by which a thick piece of metal, on a curve, is extruded into a delicate leaf-like ear is to realize the extraordinary degree of skill that underlies the smith's apparently heavy-handed manipulation of a two- or three-pound hammer.

Back once more into the fire goes the shoe, for the smith

has still a final touch or two to give it. When he whips it out again for the last time it glows dull red. He slips it round the beak and delivers a series of light taps to the under edge, so that the sharp angle is chamfered all round. There is a good reason for doing this, over and above giving his handiwork 'finish': by reducing the sharpness of the outer edge of the shoe he reduces the risk of damage to the horse's opposite foot if it has a tendency, as so many have, to allow its feet to touch as they pass one another in motion.

A final touch from the hammer to ensure that the shoe is absolutely flat and in one plane, in spite of the many processes it has been through, checked perhaps by holding up the shoe in the tongs and 'sighting' across it against the light from door or window, and it is dropped on the floor to join its predecessors or await the remainder of the set. Grey-blue, now, and with odd 'lights' on its surface reflected by its many hammered facets as the forge is blown up again for the next job, it lies there in readiness for fitting when the moment comes.

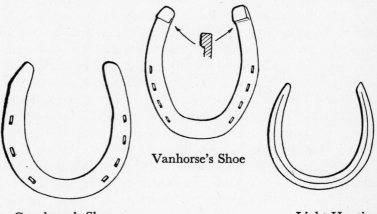

Vanhorse's Shoe

Cart-horse's Shoe

Light Hunting
Shoe

If you were to pick up that set of shoes you would find that they matched one another perfectly. Two of them would be about a quarter of an inch wider and longer than the other two, since they were made for the hind feet; but the curve, the ratio of length to breadth, would be constant. Yet at no time during the process of forging that set of shoes did the smith lay his brass rule across them, let alone check them with his calipers. He has worked by eye and feel only, once he had cut off the right length of bar.

It is almost as though his hammer has done his thinking for him, varying its weight and its point of impact instinctively. Indeed it is not much of an exaggeration to say that, on a job like this at any rate, the blacksmith works largely by instinct; he and his tools and heats form a kind of interdependent trinity, and the outcome of their collaboration is a perfectly unified and integrated product. Centuries ago he earned a farthing for each shoe he made; today it may be five shillings, or half as much again. Even that, surely, does not seem a high charge for such a demonstration of combined strength, patience, judgement and skill.

5

Shoeing the horse

Having completed his set of shoes, the smith perhaps straightens his back momentarily, drops his hammer and looks about him. Then he reaches down for his Farrier's Box.

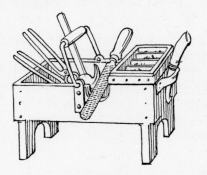

Farrier's Box

This is a simple, two-tier, open-sided affair which contains the small selection of tools required for the actual fitting of the shoe.

A shallow recess on the top 'deck', divided up by a number of low partitions, contains the various sizes of shoe nails most in use. These are tapering, rectangular nails quite different in appearance from any of the numerous other types of nail used by carpenter, joiner or cabinet-maker. Instead of having a distinct head, as most ordinary nails do, a horseshoe nail has a long, thin, flat shank, very slightly curved, tapering outwards from a sharpish flat point to a smooth-topped wedge. The nail is made of a metal as nearly as possible of the same hardness as the shoe, so that nail 'head' and shoe wear uniformly. The pseudo-head is rectangular and flat, or very slightly con-cave, fractionally larger than the widest part of the hole punched for it. When it is driven in, the metal expands, to fit exceptionally tightly against the wall of the hole; but to make doubly sure of grip, when the nail has passed out through the wall of the hoof, an inch or so above the shoe, it is 'clinched' so that it grips as securely as a rivet.

The length and thickness (particularly the length) of horseshoe nails vary con-siderably. A heavy draught horse will be fitted with shoes nailed with 'No. Twelves', three inches in length; a race-horse, on the other hand, with its much smaller hooves, takes 'No. Threes', only

Horseshoe
Nail

one and three-quarter inches long at most. Somewhere between the two comes the hunter, with a set of shoes nailed with 'No. Sixes', two and one-eighth inches in length. The smith carries a large assortment of nails, for he may shoe half a dozen different types of horse in a working day.

To emphasize the fundamental difference between ordinary nails, such as can be bought at any ironmonger's or hardware store—wire nails, ovals, cut nails, panel-pins, French nails, lost-heads and so forth—and the horseshoe nail, it is interesting to learn that at the time of the Guild Dinners, such as the annual 'Nail Makers' Dinner', the makers of horseshoe nails used to be given the distinction of a separate table to themselves. In those days, of course, all nails were

F

made by hand; the last nails to surrender to the machine age were, as might be expected, those made for fitting horseshoes.

The remainder of the space on the two decks of the farrier's box is occupied by the tools he needs for the actual shoeing. There is his special shoeing hammer, together with two or three pairs of long-reined, blunt-edged pincers, a pair of Hoof-clippers, with keen, overlapping jaws, a Buff, or Buffer, a selection of Rasps and, in a socket or clip of its own, the curiously shaped and razor-sharp Paring-knife, whose edge must not risk blunting by contact with any other tools.

The shoeing hammer is different from the heavy hammers that are used in forging. Fundamentally it is a Claw-hammer. Its head, mounted on a light, slightly curved and 'whippy' haft, has one small boss-like face opposite a strongly curved double claw. The purpose of the boss-like face is obvious: it is used to drive the nails through the shoe and into the wall of the hoof. The claw is used to twist off the point of the nail where it projects after being driven in. This particular operation, as you will see if you watch the farrier at work closely, is one of the neatest and swiftest he performs during the whole process of shoeing; it demonstrates wristwork at its most supple.

The pincers, of course, are for extracting the nails, either from the shoe if the head has worked loose (which is rare), or with the shoe attached if the two are still locked together. With its long reins and carefully designed jaws it offers an immensely powerful grip, combined with great leverage. The hoof-clippers closely resemble the pincers, but the fact that their sharpened jaws overlap, instead of butting together, enables the farrier to cut away cleanly any broken fragments of old hoof. The buff, or buffer, is a curious little tool, shaped something like an elongated capital 'H' with

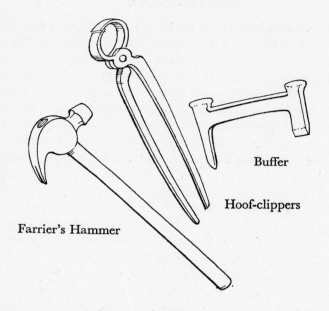

Buffer

Hoof-clippers

Farrier's Hammer

an extended central bar and thick, short uprights. It is blunt at the top and chisel-sharp at the bottom. The farrier uses it for knocking off nail 'clinches' that are too deep in the hoof wall to grip with his claw-hammer. The rasps, of course, are simply outsize files with very deep indentations and their projections staggered like the teeth of a shark. They vary greatly in their degree of roughness, each rasp having two or more 'faces', and the farrier knows at a glance just which one to use for his immediate purpose.

Finally there is the paring-knife. This is curiously shaped, with a short curved blade set in a stumpy handle. The edge of the blade is razor-sharp and finely tempered; the tip is fashioned into a sort of angled hook, something like that of a crotchet needle, but with the knife-edge inside the angle. With this the farrier can 'hook-cut' an excrescence on the hoof where rasping or a straight cut is impracticable. He prides himself, however, on using this as little as possible, for his maxim is: 'Fit the shoe to the hoof, not the hoof to the shoe.' But there are occasions when it just has to be used boldly; when, for example, the owner of the horse has delayed too long over bringing it in for shoeing and so a worn shoe has worked loose and the under side of the hoof has become uneven or cracked and split. But the slivers of hoof he cuts away will be wafer-thin; hence the extreme sharpness of the blade, which he maintains always in perfect condition.

*   *   *   *

To watch a farrier at work is a rewarding experience. It demonstrates a fine relationship between animal and man. The skill of the man, strong of muscle and infinitely patient and deliberate, is pitted against the sheer weight and strength and latent apprehension of the horse, its restlessness and its liability to react by sudden, dangerous and unpredictable movements. The farrier has learnt that no two horses are identical; every horse that comes into the smithy must be treated as an individual. He soon gets to know his 'regulars', of course; but there is always the first-timer, the unshod colt fresh from the paddock and quivering with apprehension even before it crosses the smithy threshold.

Though the farrier is a craftsman first and foremost, he must also be something of a psychologist. To watch an experienced farrier at work is to recognize this fact to the full; though I have now spent many hours in a variety of smithies I continue to be impressed by the patience and understanding that the farrier reveals in spite of the strenuousness and potential danger of his daily work.

What, in fact, is the scene presented in any smithy where shoeing is still being carried on? Tied to a wooden beam running along the end wall, or to one of a series of ring-bolts, is the horse that has been brought in for a new set of shoes. If it is a 'regular' it will be standing there completely at its ease. If it is a newcomer, or highly strung, then it will probably be a little restive, lifting and replacing first one foot and then another. Its ears will be constantly twitching at the unaccustomed sounds, the movements of strangers it cannot see because it is short-tethered. Perhaps the owner, anticipating its restlessness, has stayed with it, fondling its nose and talking to it soothingly. Possibly it will have had a nosebag fitted, in the hope that while it munches away it will gradually become more at ease. A common practice when a newcomer is to be shod is to send along with it an older horse as companion and to tie them up alongside each other. When I looked in at a smithy recently there was a high-spirited colt awaiting its first set of shoes. Tethered alongside was a plump Welsh cob, as placid as an old flower-seller at her accustomed pitch, and positively exuding encouragement.

When shoeing, the farrier usually takes the fore feet first. By starting work beneath the animal's head he will be able to reassure it; a horse is less restive when it can see what is going on, but often becomes suspicious when it is made aware of things going on 'behind its back'.

Watch the farrier's initial approach. He never hurries. Every movement he makes is deliberate, calculated. He does not snatch at the hoof and rip the old shoe away with his pincers, for that would upset even a well-accustomed horse. In any case he wants to have a good look at the worn shoe and check its 'fit' before removing it entirely; he may learn something useful from what he sees. So, first a light tap on the hoof, and the horse knows which foot is wanted. Then he lays a hand firmly on the horse's fore leg and gently slides it down towards the hoof. Curiously enough, the reflex action in almost every case is for the horse to raise its foot, and the smith then takes it in his lap, bending almost double over it as he does so, to examine it.

The shoe is worn, but not loose. He picks up his hammer and a chisel, or his buff, and strikes each clinch in turn sharply, so that it snaps off and frees the end of the nail. Then, gripping the shoe with his pincers, and working forwards from the heel of the shoe, he levers smartly, and the shoe comes away a little at a time, drawing out the nails as it does so. Two, three, four such wrenches, and the shoe falls with a thud to the ground.

Before letting go of the hoof, however, the smith cleans it, using the blunt back edge of his paring-knife to avoid damage to the foot itself. There is an accumulation of dirt to be chipped and scraped away for a start before he can assess the condition of the foot. He may also use a small pick, something like that used by the dentist to chip away tartar from his patient's teeth. If the shoe is long overdue for replacement he may have to reverse the blade of his paring-knife and carve away a horseshoe-shaped sliver of hoof to obtain a uniform surface. If the wear is too uneven he has to have recourse to his hoof-clippers. But he must be extremely careful to see that the 'frog' of the foot—the central muscular pad which is the mainspring of the animal's means of locomotion—is not damaged in any way, and that the rest of the foot, or 'sole', within the quarter-inch-thick horny wall is in good condition.

Satisfied at last that all is as it should be, he turns next to the fitting of the shoe. If the horse is one of his 'regulars' the set will probably have been forged already and be hanging over a nail in the wall or one of the beams. If, on the other hand, it is a first-timer, then its new shoes will be forged in pairs and fitted in pairs. This gives the unaccustomed horse a chance to rest between whiles, and enables the farrier, too, to 'rest'—at least in so far as a change of occupation from fitting to forging may be called resting. But each shoe in turn will probably have to be heated slightly so that any final adjustment can be made with a light hammer blow and the hot iron will bed down well beneath the hoof. The farrier calls this 'seating' the shoe.

The shoe, then, is taking its heat. When he is ready for it the farrier's assistant plucks it from the hearth with his tongs, drops it on to the anvil to shake off any scale that may have accumulated on it, drives a punch into one of the holes and passes it over. Now comes the moment which is likeliest to startle the unaccustomed horse, and incidentally produce the smell that some people dislike, though the smith has long since ceased to be conscious of it: the acrid and pungent smell of burning hoof, accompanied by thick, curling, grey-blue smoke. For the hot shoe has just been placed on the under side of the hoof, now turned upwards between the farrier's knees. He holds it there steadily with his punch, checking its position by the set of the clip. The process may startle, but it does not hurt the animal in the slightest for the horn of which the wall of the hoof consists is completely insensitive, like the human fingernail.

As he confidently anticipated, the fit is almost perfect. Almost, but perhaps not absolutely. So, he drops the hoof, not to the ground but on to the smooth and polished ball top of his Farrier's Stand, a tripod perhaps eighteen inches high specially designed for this purpose. And the horse remains there, one fore foot raised, as though about to mount a flight of steps.

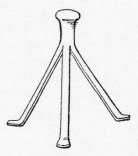

Farrier's Stand

Back into the hearth goes the shoe. The farrier has noted the exact point at which the curve is to be reduced or extended. A dull red heat, and a blow or two of the hand-hammer, and now the curve has been adjusted. He tests the shoe once again; once again the acrid fumes swirl about his head and the sharp hiss of hot metal on horn makes itself heard. This time there is no doubt that the fit is perfect. The farrier drops the shoe to the ground to cool off, and proceeds to remove the second shoe while it does so.

At last all four hooves have been prepared. He does not use the stand for the hind feet. It is not that the stand is not strong enough to hold their weight; it is simply that shoeing the hind feet is a more exacting task altogether, and because the farrier is working out of the horse's range of vision there is a risk that it may become restive. If it lashes out suddenly —as is often the case with a first-timer or any high-spirited animal—then the iron stand would be sent flying across the smithy, to injure anyone in its line of flight. For this reason the farrier prefers to be his own 'stand' while working on the hind feet.

It is a tough and exacting job. There is far more weight in a horse's hind legs than in its fore legs, and owing to the conformation of its joints and the weight of the haunches above them the hind leg is a troublesome thing to handle. Even an experienced farrier, dealing with a horse he knows well, approaches its hind legs with caution. Something entirely unexpected may happen: a stinging fly, for instance, may settle on some sensitive part of the horse's anatomy; a car may backfire in the road just outside the smithy; a sudden noise may be made by someone working at the forge. It does not take much to startle even the most placid horse, and its instinctive reflex action is to let fly with the hoof that is not taking its weight at the moment.

The smith knows this, and is always prepared for it.

Notice how he stands in relation to the horse. He crouches almost beneath its haunch, with his back to it, the upturned hind foot in his lap. If the horse does lash out suddenly that hoof flies backwards—that is to say outwards and away from the smith. He may, of course, try to hold on to it with both hands, if only to maintain contact with the horse and assert his authority. If it is a colt, or small horse, and the smith is strong, he may succeed, though the effort may lift him to his feet and set him swaying convulsively, both hands gripping the hoof for all he is worth. But if it is a big horse, or if he is a fraction of a second late in his own reactions, and still hangs on, he may well be lifted off the ground and sent flying across the smithy floor, to end up against the forge or the anvil and badly injured.

This rarely happens. The experienced farrier knows when to let go. He has an uncanny sense of perception; he weighs up his animal and takes no chances. I have seen a farrier tossed about like an empty sack in a strong wind, but he has always mastered the horse in time. He never does this by harshness or brutality; a good farrier would scorn to use violence of any kind against a horse. For that matter, he rarely, if ever, raises his voice, and he never abuses a horse whatever the treatment he receives from it. This is where his knowledge of psychology comes in: he knows that he is dealing with a creature that in many ways is like a primitive adult or a young child. To shout or swear at it would only increase its alarm and fear and excite it to more violent reactions.

When dealing with any restive or nervous animal he keeps up a running monologue for its benefit throughout the operation. He does not use many words; indeed, it does not particularly matter what those words are. The real value lies in the soothing quality of his voice, and the fact that it is there all the time—a sustained communication between animal and man. 'There's a good boy,' he says, in a low voice little more than a murmur. 'There's a good boy. . . . There's my little man. . . . There's a good boy. . . .' And so on, repeated over and over again in a voice muffled by contact with the horse's flank.

There is a soothing quality in his voice, which the animal hears coming from somewhere down beneath its own belly. Watch its ears as it stands there on the smithy floor, tethered to that ring-bolt. They are pricked forward and then backward. They respond to the farrier's low-pitched murmur and provide evidence of the effect it has. If the horse is momentarily frightened and makes a sudden movement the pitch of the farrier's murmur remains unchanged; he continues his gentle verbal persuasion, and the horse becomes quiet again. The farrier may not even be aware that he is talking as he works, but the horse is very conscious of it indeed and ordinarily responds just as a small child does to the soothing words of its mother when it is frightened or in pain.

Now comes the time for the actual shoeing (see plate opposite page 49). The farrier has drawn his box of tools close to hand, though not within reach of the hoof. Once more he places his hand on the horse's hind leg and runs it gently but firmly downwards to the hoof. As before, the horse responds by lifting its hoof till the farrier can cradle it on the tough leather apron on his lap. He does not, of course, use the stand at this stage, for he must have the hoof upside down in order to drive the nails home.

He starts at the front of the shoe, inserting a nail of suitable length in the hole nearest the clip. Listen to the rhythm of his hammer blows as he works: it is a curiously musical 'hard-soft, hard-soft' repeated over and over again. The first blow strikes the nail squarely on the head, the second so lightly that it is hardly more than an echo of the first; the third is another firm blow, the fourth another 'echo'. A fifth and a sixth follow, and a final flourish of blows, and the nail has been driven well home into the countersunk, wedge-shaped hole in the shoe, and the tip of the nail has emerged an inch or so from the wall.

You may have noticed that a horseshoe nail is not only very delicately tapered but also, on its flat side, very slightly curved throughout its whole length. This curve is deliberate, for the nail is designed to be driven into the hoof in a curving path in such a way that its tip emerges from the wall about an inch above the upper edge of the shoe. It is a popular fallacy that a horse's hoof is solid. On the contrary, it consists of little more than a wall, or shell, of horn, perhaps a quarter of an inch in thickness. The ratio of horn to flesh and muscle and bone is much the same as that of the finger-nail to the human finger. So, if the nail were not driven in on an outward curve, it would pass inside the wall and severely damage the horse's foot, quite certainly laming it, perhaps for life.

You will notice that the farrier listens attentively as he drives in each nail: he can actually tell by the sound of his hammer whether the nail is penetrating the wall of the hoof as it should. If his ear tells him it is not he whips it out at once, before it has gone too far, and inserts another, tapping it with even more care and concentration. Never on any account does he insert the same nail a second time. The protruding end is not, of course, left. With a turn of his wrist the farrier grips it with the claws of his hammer and snaps it cleanly off. A smart tap of the hammer head on the twisted tip, and that nail is dealt with: the glancing action, followed by a straight blow, has 'clinched' the nail, riveting it to the hoof. The familiar and expressive saying, 'That clinches it', is yet another which derives from the smithy.

Now the operation of shoeing is almost complete; it

remains only to finish off. The farrier takes up a rasp, lays
it across the wall of the hoof where the row of clinches
protrudes and smooths them off until the convex surface is
free from projections, whether of horn or of metal. The rasp
is used sparingly, and with discretion, and never higher up
the hoof than the clinches. This is because under the rasp the
horn tends to lose its natural oil and the surface quickly
deteriorates if it loses too much. To compensate for un-
avoidable loss the farrier takes a small tin and, with a short,
stiff-bristled brush, 'paints' the new-shod hooves with neat's-
foot oil, or with some concoction of his own devising, such as
a blend of linseed oil and Stockholm tar.

The job is done at last. The smith, careful first to replace
in his farrier's box any tools he may have dropped on the
floor, slides the box out of harm's way, straightens his back
and wipes his brow. He has expended a good deal of
concentrated energy. The horse, too, stirs and stretches,
relieved that the job is done. He half turns his head to look
at the man who has been shoeing him, whose voice has kept
up that continuous flow of soothing words throughout the
long operation. He stamps on the smithy floor, first with
one hoof, then with another, almost as though trying the feel
of his new footwear.

The smith pats him on shoulder or haunch. 'Good boy,' he
says again. 'Good lad!' Even though he may have been tossed
hither and yon, though he has been holding a hind foot
pressed downwards into his lap by a leg weighing not far
short of a hundredweight, though the sweat is still glistening
on his brow and he is still breathing hard from his sustained
exertions, he yet has a word for the horse he has just shod.
However exacting the job has been, he bears him not the
slightest ill-will.

Meanwhile there is another horse waiting; another set of
shoes to heat and fit and hammer home. And after that

another, and yet another, and another after that. There may at one time be a couple of horses tethered inside the smithy and three or four more tethered to ring-bolts outside the smithy door, impatiently awaiting their turn. And even if there are no horses actually waiting for him there are always sets of shoes to be forged in readiness for when they do put in an appearance.

*　　　　*　　　　*　　　　*

When the farrier goes out on what he calls 'cold-shoeing'—that is to say, visiting his clients' horses in their stables or loose-boxes—he takes with him not only the shoes he has already forged for them, according to measurements he has already obtained, but a good many spare sets of shoes as well, all approximately the same size and shape. This is a sensible precaution, for however good his memory, however accurate that photographic eye of his, there is always the possibility of a mistake, and a farrier's time is valuable. There is also the chance that there may prove to be an additional horse or two to shoe, not mentioned when his services were asked for.

He drives himself about in a Land-Rover or estate car, into which he can pile the many miscellaneous articles he is likely to need in the several hours that may elapse before his last visit is made and he can return to the smithy. There will be a small portable anvil—possibly made out of a short section of 'H'-shaped steel girder; and a farrier's stand, of course—for no farrier wastes his strength and the stand saves him a good deal of back-breaking effort when shoeing. His anvil hammers, with the possible exception of one general-purpose hammer, he leaves behind him in the smithy, together with his tongs, punches, pritchels and stamps. But he takes with him his farrier's hammer and the essential

hoof-clippers and pincers, buffer, rasps and paring-knife.
And, of course, a wide assortment of horseshoe nails.

His main 'anvil', when shoeing—whether in the smithy
or not—will be his knees, protected by the thick leather
apron that is an essential feature of every smith's outfit.
People talk of the complaint 'Housemaid's Knee'; I have
never heard a smith complain of 'Farrier's Knee', though
such a complaint would be well justified. For it is his knees,
or rather the muscular part of the top of his thighs immediately above his knees, that serves him for anvil. It must be
about the toughest part of his anatomy! Not only does it
have to hold the weight, often the very restless weight, of a
horse's hoof; it has also to withstand the repeated hammer
blows as he drives in one nail after another. The leather
apron, in which the hoof is snuggled, may absorb a fraction
of the impact, but it can only be a fraction at best.

Inevitably, working in a stable or on the paved terrace
outside it, the farrier is at something of a disadvantage. He
lacks the amenities of his well-equipped smithy. Ask any
farrier whether he prefers travelling out to his clients or
dealing with them, as it were, in his own 'surgery', and you
will be left in no doubt as to which he prefers.

Working away from the smithy necessarily calls for a good
deal of improvisation. It is interesting to watch how cleverly
the farrier makes his tools serve purposes for which they were
not originally intended. For example, he finds that one shoe,
or perhaps a whole set of shoes, is not quite wide enough for
the hooves for which they were designed. They are, perhaps,
an eighth of an inch too narrow at the widest part of the
curve. If they were too wide, on the other hand, it would
be the simplest thing in the world to set them on the edge
of his portable anvil, give them a smart blow or two and
so reduce them to the exactly required cross-dimensions.
But to expand them, cold, is a problem with not quite

such an obvious solution. Nevertheless he has found the answer.

What does he do? He inserts the jaws of his stoutest pair of pincers or his hoof-clippers between the open ends of the heel of the shoe. The outside curve of the pincer jaws makes contact with the inner face of the shoe tips. The farrier proceeds to force the reins of his pincers apart. They afford him enormous leverage. The shoe yields slowly but surely to the pressure exerted upon it from inside, expanding the required fraction of an inch, so that when he next tries it against the hoof it is exact. The solution to the problem is simple common sense, a lesson in improvisation. The process calls for sound judgement as well as sheer muscle; but then no one demonstrates this combination more consistently than the blacksmith does, whatever the operation he is engaged on.

Those massive pincers serve another purpose, too. Their boldly curved and rounded jaws afford quite a useful miniature portable anvil. When the farrier has lifted the horse's foot on to his stand for the final clinching and trimming of the nails and hoof he inserts the pincers underneath the shoe so that when he hammers on the nail ends the hoof is not taking the full impact. This is important, for the under side of the foot, within the wall, particularly the sole and the frog, is tender and easily damaged or bruised.

Though generally speaking the farrier prefers to work on a horse in his own smithy, he does recognize one advantage in visiting it 'at home'. If it is a first-timer, or a restless, high-spirited horse, he will have a better chance of shoeing it without undue trouble because there will be none of the background noises of other smiths at work, of bellows and flaring forge, of hammers on anvils and the high-speed whine of a bench drill to upset it. Also, the human beings the horse is most accustomed to will probably be moving about the loose-boxes and will be available to hold the animal's head if need be. There may also be familiar stable companions, and the delectable smell of a rack of hay: all inducements to remain still and permit the farrier to get the irksome job completed.

There is one curious aspect of this home shoeing that may take you, as it did me the first time, entirely by surprise. There were two cocker spaniels wandering about on the terrace where I watched shoeing being done on a Sussex estate. To my astonishment, the instant any piece of old hoof fell to the ground the two dogs dashed forward to within inches of the horse's hooves to scramble for the prize represented by a fragment of horn. If ever I saw a look of triumph on a successful dog's face and a look of chagrin on that of the loser, then that was the occasion!

All dogs regard the clippings of a horse's hoof as a prize delicacy. Yet you will never see a dog in a smithy—at any rate while the forge is in operation. Why? Because all dogs are frightened of sparks, and the smithy is therefore no place for them. But on their home ground they can expect 'pickings' without having to run the gauntlet of a shower of sparks to snatch them up. The farrier may prefer working on his own home ground; the dogs prefer him to visit theirs.

*　　　*　　　*　　　*

To a large extent, and for obvious reasons, a blacksmith, whether he is a farrier as well or not, is his own master. He has always been among the most independent of craftsmen. He works not so much to set hours as to the changing demands of the day. If there are horses to be shod on whom the farmer depends absolutely for a job of ploughing (though there are few plough teams to be seen in these days of the ubiquitous tractor) then he will gladly start work early in the

Two eighteenth-century wrought-iron brackets

(Victoria and Albert Museum. Crown Copyright)

A chandelier rod from a church. Seventeenth century

morning, or continue late in the evening, in order to satisfy his client. If there is a hunter to be fitted with a set of light-weight shoes for a meet the next day, then the farrier will find, or make, the time to do the job. If there is a race-horse among his clientele to be fitted with the special aluminium race-horse 'plates' before being taken by horse-box to the venue of the race for which he is entered, then somehow, some time, the farrier will contrive to get them made and fitted.

Such a job will certainly demand much more time than the fitting of a standard set of shoes. To begin with they are so light, so fragile (fit to serve just for a single race or two, on turf), that they call for great delicacy and sureness in hand-ling. The inner curve of each shoe will probably have to be shaped, or cut away, at the heel to prevent the risk of damage to the opposing foot when the horse is at full stretch; and there are other subtle refinements that vary from horse to horse, even from shoe to shoe. But the farrier takes pride in challenges such as these and meets them as they come along.

He has his 'perks', as well as his price. If a race-horse or hunter that has been shod by him does well he can reasonably anticipate a pound note or two from the well-satisfied owner, who will certainly have recognized the fact that his mount's success is partly due to the skilful forging and fitting of those all-important shoes. If an unshod colt is brought in for its first shoeing it is traditional to reward the farrier for the extra trouble (and danger) he will almost certainly have experienced by standing him a bottle of beer. In the old days, a heavy and perhaps restless draught horse, capable of throwing the farrier around the smithy like a shuttlecock, would often mean the leaving of a small barrel of beer in the smithy for the farrier and his mate to cool down with after the horse had stamped away. Such traditions survive, even if they are not invariably observed.

G

The shoeing-smith is to a large extent his own master in
that he can pick and choose his work, since he is in such
demand. Even if he is employed by someone else he remains
an individualist, working at the speed best suited to him and
selecting his work according to some inscrutable code of his
own. A generation or two back a smithy would very often
be a 'factory-in-miniature', so great would be the demands
for blacksmithing in a particular district. There is a good
picture of one such smithy, painted by an old blacksmith
who died a few years ago. He was recalling working con-
ditions as they were in his younger days, soon after the turn
of the century:

Nine of us worked at the smithy. Two of us did nothing all day
but shoeing. The day started at 6 in the morning and went on
till 6 in the evening—even till 7 at times. The guv'nor, the master-
smith, were an old man, over 80. In his later years he didn't
come into the smithy until after breakfast. The first man in the
smithy in the morning had to pick up a hammer and strike the
anvil three times—just to let the old man know we were on
the job.

I was always on shoeing. Until the horses started coming in,
three of us would be shoe making: two strikers and a smith. We
took two old shoes, heated them and hammered them together,
the strikers striking alternately, the smith holding the shoe on
the anvil and using the small hammer himself. During the 12-
hour day the two of us aimed to do 36 shoes, that is 9 horses.
Two of us averaged four shoes an hour. The town horses came
in every three weeks for re-shoeing. Country horses, that worked
chiefly on the land, came in once in three months. The town
horses were nearly always leg-weary, and so harder to shoe.
They'd lie on you as you lifted their leg.

In frosty weather we had to 'rough' the horses. There are two
kinds of 'roughing'. You can either put frost-nails in the shoes,
or you can take the shoes off and turn the heels and toes up.
There was a queue of horses one particular day, half way down

the street, all waiting to be roughed. It was the day of the Stowmarket Xmas Sale. We did 107 horses that day! When we finished I were just taking off my apron when I saw two more horses that had been sent up to be shod. We had no shoes left for them, so my mate and I had to set to and make the shoes and shoe them. It was eight o'clock gone when we finished. I was so tired I had to get off my bike twice on the way home and sit on the side of the road in the snow for a spell before I could go on. We'd worked from 6.30 till 8.0, with only the shortest of breaks during the day. As my mate was over seventy I couldn't let him lift a horse's foot after knocking-off time, so I actually shod those last two horses single-handed. That was the sort of day you don't forget!

That smith explained elsewhere in his story just why they had the practice of taking old shoes, heating them red-hot, then folding them over on themselves sandwich-wise and hammering them together. New iron, he maintained, was too soft to make good shoes: 'It was too soft. The more you hammer iron, the tougher it gets, so old shoes welded and hammered together last much longer.' And he added: 'They don't do that today; it takes too long.'

In fact this practice has not been entirely abandoned. I have seen a smith carry out the operation more than once, for some special job. To watch him heat an old, worn, battered shoe, 'fold' it, hammer it and evolve from it a 'new' shoe, of smaller dimensions but perfectly in scale and pro- portion, is to be witness to a small miracle. It is a pleasing variant of 'New lamps for old'. You might think that after many years a farrier would have lost interest in his trade; a forge, an anvil and a hammer, after all, suggest a monotonous sort of life. In fact, there is a great deal of variety in the day's work even of a man whose sole occupation is shoeing horses. There are, to begin with, so many different types of horse to shoe: every type, from shires and other heavy draught horses to colts and cobs, hunters and race-horses. Only the other day when I was in my favourite smithy the farrier was called out to go and shoe one of the Queen Mother's stallions, at grass in a paddock not many miles away. It was not the first time he had obeyed the summons, either.

There are the 'surgical', or 'pathological', shoes that he has to make. These are jobs that involve experimentation and can result in some very unusual shoes indeed. At first glance they may not seem any different from standard shoes; a more careful glance, however, will reveal that in fact the heel of the shoe has been made thicker than the toe—a device intended to counteract some malformation of the hoof and throw the weight further forward to relieve it. Again, if the hoof suffers from what is known as Sandcrack a specially shaped shoe must be forged and fitted to reduce the pressure on that particular area of the foot.

Again, perhaps the all-important 'frog', which actuates a deep-seated valvular movement in the blood circulation by a form of massage induced by the upward pressure of the road surface on the muscle, has become misshapen; a special shoe must be designed and forged to compensate for this. The farrier may forge what he refers to as a 'T'-shoe, which resembles a capital 'T' except that the cross-bar is slightly rounded and bent downwards. Sometimes a shoe is fitted with an actual cross-bar linking the two tips so as to give additional support to the heel of the hoof.

Again, though all four feet may appear, and in fact be, perfectly normal the owner may have found that his horse shows a tendency to 'click'; that is to say, the hind foot catches up with and tends to trip the matching fore foot. Nothing, of course, can be done with the animal's muscular system to correct this; but a skilful shaping and adjustment of a set of shoes may do much to minimize the effect of the fault, even though it cannot eradicate it entirely. The hind shoes will be so designed as to retard the forward movement of the hoof, while the fore shoes will be so designed as slightly to accelerate the movement of the front hooves. It is largely a question of weight and balance, and perhaps a 'rolled' forward edge on two of the shoes will encourage the wearer to lift them a fraction more quickly and so avoid the 'tripping' action.

In cases like these—and there is an almost infinite variety of them, each requiring its own specific treatment—the farrier and the vet may collaborate, and many a horse that seemed for one reason or another in danger of going lame thus receives a new lease of active life. In fact, any good farrier is to some extent a vet, even if he has not sat for the examinations that would qualify him. Long experience has given him a remarkably thorough overall knowledge of complaints common to horses, and many a country farrier is every bit as expert in diagnosis and treatment as a qualified veterinary surgeon. He picks up from him such technical terms and disease names as Ringbone, Sandcrack, Dropped Sole, Ankylosis and many others, though he may already have his own names for these complaints. Through close and sustained contact with a wide variety of horses he learns a great deal about their anatomy; and learns it perhaps the best way: by study of the living animal rather than from a textbook.

Some farriers, however, have felt it worth while to study this aspect of their trade both from textbooks and in classes held by instructors, as well as by practice in their smithies. A farrier may sit for a series of examinations, each one a stage more advanced than the last, that entitle him to a row of letters after his name, like those of a doctor or dentist. But he may not trouble to put the letters after his name on the signboard over his smithy door. You may know a farrier for years and never even guess that he has taken those

examinations and qualified. In any case his wide circle of
clients, whether farmers, tradesmen, riding-school proprietors
or owners of hacks, hunters or race-horses, are not much concerned about such credentials. They know he is a good man,
he has shod and cared for their horses, perhaps for half a
lifetime; as they might say: 'What he doesn't know about
shoeing isn't worth learning!'

The simplest examination is the one that qualifies a smith
as a 'Registered Doorman'. It is the starting grade of farrier,
one that involves little more than routine. He works for the
master farrier, accepting the horses in what is often called the
Pent-house and preparing them for shoeing. Later he becomes a 'Registered Shoeing Smith', a title which is self-
explanatory. If he is ambitious he may take a further
examination, success in which entitles him to the letters
A.F.C.L.—'Associate of the Farriers Company of London'.
There is another, and much more advanced, examination
he can take if he wishes to. In order to pass this he will have
to show that he possesses knowledge not far short of that of a
qualified veterinary surgeon. He can then add to his name
the letters F.W.C.F.—'Fellow of the Worshipful Company
of Farriers'. He is then among the élite in his trade.

Even a perfunctory glance through an examination paper
such as he will have to tackle in order to win this final distinction is enough to astonish the unthinking person who has
always assumed the blacksmith to be nothing more than a
heavily built, sinewy individual who puts new shoes on
horses in the smoky, noisy, dark and old-fashioned workshop
known as a smithy. Consider some of the questions, taken at
random from an examination paper, together with the
detailed answers he must be able to give:

Q. What are the parts of the hoof that can be seen? A. The
Wall, the Bars, the Coronary Frog Band, the Sole, the Frog,

the White Line. In some cases of over-grown hooves a few of the Horny Laminae may be seen on the inner part of the Wall projecting below the level of the Sole.

Q. What bones are there within the hoof? A. The Os Pedis, in the front portion; the Navicular at the back of the Os Pedis; part of the Os Coronae, above the Os Pedis and Navicular Bone.

Q. What else is there inside the hoof besides bones? A. The Ligaments; the terminal portion of the Tendons which flex the Foot; the Blood Vessels and Nerves; the Plantar Cushion, between the Frog and the Perforans Tendon; the Lateral Cartilages; the Navicular Bursae; the Sensitive Laminae which dovetail with the Horny Laminae on the inner surface of the Wall.

Q. What percentage of water is contained in (a) the Wall, (b) the Sole, (c) the Frog? A. 24%; 32%; 42%.

Those are but a handful of the scores of searching questions that a farrier must be able to answer if he is to reach the highest degree of qualification. Few farriers bother to take the examination; yet in all probability they are every bit as expert in their craft as they would be had they spent many tedious hours with textbooks open in front of them. Practice has made them, if not 'perfect', yet at least so shrewd in diagnosing symptoms, and so resourceful and competent in relieving or curing them, that they can be confidently relied upon to fulfil the innumerable exacting tasks that confront them daily in their smithies throughout their working lives.

6

The artist-craftsman

BLACKSMITHS were working at their forges in many
parts of the world for centuries before they began to turn
their hands to making horseshoes; they were 'farriers' because they worked in *ferrum*—iron—not because they fitted
this all-purpose metal to horses' hooves. In fact, they were
'general smiths'—as the great majority of them are to this
day.

The general smith has always been an important factor in
a community whose requirements continuously increase in
complexity. He is a 'man of iron', as he has always been; and
iron is the basic ingredient of most of the material objects
owned and used by the community. The farmers' tractors,
harrows, seed-drills, binders, combine-harvesters, pitchforks,
tow-bars, hay-elevators, hand-scythes and other gear are all
of iron or mild steel; and, as such, are all liable to distortion
and fracture, to require the replacement of small parts and
general overhaul and maintenance. The man who works in
iron, who knows its strength and weakness and potentialities,
who can make and fit anything from a small rivet to a massive axle or tow-bar, who can remove, weld and replace a
section of a combine-harvester's main wheel, build a new
axle for a dung-cart or trailer, or forge and fit new strakes to a
tractor wheel—he is the man on whom the farmer depends
if he is to keep going. The roadman's scythe and sickle, the
shepherd's crook in a sheep-farming district, the house-
holder's lawn-mower, the timber-feller's chains, crowbars

and other heavy tackle: all these, and other needs too numerous to list, are filled by the aptly termed general smith.

It always has been so. Legendary smiths, whether in Greece, Rome, Scandinavia or further afield, forged the thunderbolts of the gods, the shields and armour of the heroes, and the swords, daggers, spears, maces, cutlasses and iron clubs they wielded against their enemies. In medieval and earlier times, when every fighting-man wore chain-mail or some other form of body armour, and even the war-horses were protected by mail, it was the smith who forged all the equipment.

He forged also a great deal of the heavy domestic ware, as the housewives' needs became more elaborate. The poker, shovel and tongs, the heavy iron pots and cauldrons, the pot-hooks, spits and hearth-cranes for swinging them over the open fire; the humble grates and the fire-dogs that held massive logs on the rich man's hearth; the iron rails that protected his children from the danger of the great fires, the grilles over his windows that prevented unlawful entry and theft, the hinges on the doors, the iron nails that pinned the great oak beams, the bands and hoops that gave strength and rigidity to wooden and stone containers, whether of stores or of wealth; the cramps and dowels used to knit masonry together—but the list is endless. And though the shape and design of many of these articles may have changed over the years, nevertheless many of them still fulfil exactly the same function and call for much the same kind of maintenance.

The greater part of the blacksmith's craft throughout the ages has of course been almost entirely utilitarian: he has been engaged upon making and repairing articles that are in everyday use and possession of which is essential to the owners' way of life. He forged weapons and armour designed

to make the owner an efficient and, so far as was practicable,
invulnerable fighting man; he forged implements, tools and
utensils designed to function efficiently and to stand up as
long as possible to the inevitable wear and tear of daily use.

*   *   *   *

But there is latent in every craftsman an instinct to turn
out a product possessing qualities other than the purely
functional or utilitarian. The true craftsman is nearly always
something of an artist too. It is instinctive with him to
impart some beauty—simple or ornate according to the
fashion of the period in which he works—to the objects that
come from his hands. No potter, for example, is ever content
merely to turn out an indefinite number of identical pots or
bowls of the simplest possible shape; he infuses something
of himself into the clay on which he works, just as the
sculptor gives something of himself to the stone or grained
wood that constitutes his raw material.

This attitude towards his work is certainly true of the
blacksmith, who handles what is probably the most intract-
able raw material worked by any artist-craftsman. He has
always imparted an individual touch to his handiwork,
whether in its overall design or in some detail that only the
keen observer might detect. Many smiths, particularly
during the great age of blacksmithery, actually put their
'signature' to their work, sometimes in the form of a stamped
initial on, for example, the base of the main upright of a
wrought-iron gate or grille. So may an artist sign a picture
he has painted or a sculptor a statue he has carved.

Many of the finest examples of the blacksmith's craft down
the centuries, though, bear such unmistakable marks of the
identity of their creator that an expert can recognize and
identify them by their design and workmanship without

needing to look for an actual signature. The 'signature' is to be seen in the workmanship itself, just as it is in the brushwork on the canvases of the world's great painters or in the tooling of a sculptor's masterpieces.

It would be easy to illustrate this from a variety of aspects of the blacksmith's craft. Perhaps one of the most interesting illustrations could be taken from the long tradition of blacksmithery as demonstrated in the form of wrought-iron gates. It is a good illustration, too, for the designing and forging of such gates is a tradition that not only goes back many hundreds of years but is very much alive today, so that comparisons may be easily made. These gates possess such notable features that unusual steps have been taken to preserve specimens in this country and in France (where some of the most outstanding are to be found) and elsewhere on the Continent where such examples of wrought ironwork are prized among the major works of art.

It is true that for obvious reasons you will not find many of the older gates still *in situ*, but rather in galleries, notably in the Victoria and Albert Museum in London. But you will certainly find, scattered about the country today, notable examples of the blacksmith's craft in this particular field that have been commissioned in the last century or two. Many connoisseurs of wrought ironwork take keen pleasure in seeking out these ornamental gates and grilles and balustrades and photographing (or drawing) them, so that they gradually build up their own personal picture gallery of examples that have particularly appealed to them. Whole books, too, have been devoted to the inexhaustible subject of 'Ornamental Wrought Ironwork'.

The blacksmiths who produced the oldest surviving specimens of this work naturally lacked the resources available to their descendants, the master smiths of the eighteenth, nineteenth and twentieth centuries. The most cursory glance at the relatively few surviving specimens of this very early work shows this. But though their resources may have been limited, their enterprise and their imagination, as well as their skill, were abundant.

Of course, practically no examples survive from the pre-Roman period, or the period of the Roman occupation; and for some time afterwards there seems to have been a lull in the smith's activities, both in Britain and in Europe as a whole. At that time the Continent was being inundated by a succession of barbaric tribes from the east, and many crafts, including that of metal-working, were temporarily submerged beneath these destroying waves. Only Northern Europe seems to have escaped. It is to this fact, and to the fact that Britain was later invaded by these same men from the North—the Norsemen—that we owe our renewed tradition of blacksmithery. For the Norsemen, particularly the Danish Goths, were remarkably skilful workers in metal, and when they rowed their longships up our estuaries they brought with them their skills—to our eventual profit.

You may wonder what evidence exists to show that we owe this debt to a race of men who brought devastation to much of our land and despair to so many of its inhabitants ten centuries and more ago. In fact the evidence is positive and clear cut; it is presented quite unmistakably in the wrought ironwork of an ancient church door at Stillingfleet in Yorkshire. Take a good look at that church door. It is, of course, made of timber; but the timbers are reinforced by ironwork, and that ironwork certainly strikes one as ornamental rather than purely functional. The timbers are upright, and are bonded together by a series of horizontal 'straps', two of which are continuous from the hinge, or 'hanging', side to the opposite side, while others are apparently 'tacked on' at random. In one or two cases these may originally have been joined together in one continuous

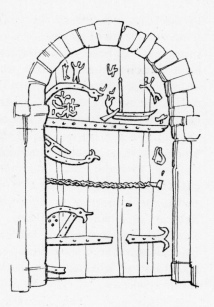

Drawing of a church door
at Stillingfleet, in Yorkshire,
showing wrought ironwork

strap, though this is by no means obvious or necessarily the
case.

What is, however, almost immediately obvious is that the
man who forged that ironwork was either a Norseman himself or a Briton who had come very strongly under Norse
influence. The evidence for this lies mainly in the top right-
hand panel of the door. For there, quite unmistakably, is a
representation in iron of—a Viking longship! It has the
boldly upswept stem that characterized those ancient
vessels—in one of which Leif Eriksson discovered America
centuries before Columbus or Amerigo Vespucci crossed the
Atlantic. It even has the great sweeping 'steer-board', the
earliest form of rudder which gave us our term 'starboard'.

Smaller details confirming the impression that this ironwork was forged under Viking influence are to be found in
the 'dragon heads' that form the terminations of several of

the curved and other straps. Since the earliest times in Scandinavia those dragon heads have dominated the long-ships, and also the gable-ends of the *stavkirken*, or timber-built churches, some of which, though a thousand years old, are still in use as churches to this day.

It is interesting to note how the functional and the ornamental were combined even in those distant days. The man who forged the ironwork for the Stillingfleet church door knew well that its main function was to give strength to the timbers, to bond them together into one. In his day the church was not only a place of worship, it was a sanctuary; and it was important therefore to make it as nearly impregnable as possible. So, the hinges were extended right across the door—just as they are today in church doors, garage and workshop and stable doors and indeed any doors of unusual width and weight, to unite the timbers and impart strength to the whole.

But this particular blacksmith was obviously something of an artist as well as a craftsman, and he used the excuse of hinge- and strap-making to give play to his ingenuity in ornamentation. He set a Viking longship in one part of the door—modelled on one that he had perhaps seen coming up the Ouse not far from Stillingfleet, or in which possibly he had crossed the grey North Sea before taking to himself a native woman, marrying and settling down, to be absorbed into the community at last.

Whimsically, he forged also a few diminutive human figures, scattering them about the timberwork. One of them looks as though he is performing on an invisible trampoline; two others in the opposite portion of the door are apparently shouting for joy, or registering surprise, by waving their upraised arms. And below these he has placed what might be a human limb or two, disjointed and discarded—hacked off, perhaps, by a Viking sword during battle.

What else is there? You can detect a curious horizontal band of ironwork, in appearance rather like a chain, but not connected with either hinge, though it spans the door from one side to the other. More interesting, though, are the two great arcs of ironwork (the lower one broken off short) which serve no obviously useful function but impart a richness, even a flamboyance, to the door which is most engaging. They are great, bold curves of iron, sweeping outwards from the hinges themselves and then curving back again towards the straps. You will notice that the termination of each arc is the Viking dragon head, a pagan symbol with a grim significance for anyone unlucky enough to fall foul of these ruthless invaders.

Not many specimens of the blacksmith's craft survive today that are as old as this church door at Stillingfleet. Later examples of hinges and other door 'furniture' show a truer sense of pattern, greater symmetry, perhaps even more imagination; but this is only to be expected, for as time went by the spirit of emulation increased, successive generations of blacksmiths had the inspiration and example of their predecessors' work to influence them, and so a permanent challenge to produce something finer than any that had gone before. Ornamental wrought ironwork down the centuries demonstrates this to the full, and clearly shows that you do not have to scratch the craftsman very deeply before you reach the artist within.

During the centuries immediately following the arrival of the Norsemen, with the knowledge of metal-working which they so quickly imparted to the Britons among whom they settled, there was a remarkable upsurge of creative forging, and hammers rang on anvils over more and more of the country as the inspiration spread in ever-widening circles. The work of these blacksmiths is to be found widely distributed. Much of it survives to this day in the place where it was wrought; much else has been rescued from slow deterioration due to weather and other factors and is now safely housed in museums, lacquered or otherwise treated with unobtrusive preservatives so that it has a good chance of surviving for centuries to come. Now all those who take delight in looking at examples of fine craftsmanship can visit those galleries and wander through them at their leisure.

*   *   *   *

One of the most distinguished master smiths alive today, a man who not only knows how to forge iron but can write about his craft with both authority and a strong poetic urge, has put into words something of what underlies this strange power of iron to draw the best out of the men who work it in the forge and on the anvil (a sort of echo of primitive Man's secret relationship with the 'magic metal'):

The early smiths mostly had an understanding and deep respect for the material in which they worked; one has only to examine their work superficially to see that they did not expect or attempt to make iron do impossible things, to strain it beyond its true capabilities. Their work is spontaneous and lively—due to the fact that it was invariably worked at white or red heat, and accordingly required quick decisions for the application of each hammer blow. This gives such work its dynamic quality, its essentiality and freedom from fussiness. That spirit of urgency is the essential of all true blacksmithery. Iron that has been heated and beaten into shape at the anvil by a sensitive blacksmith seems to grow, to be alive. Sinuous arms thread their way like tendrils through labyrinthine panels, terminating in scrolls that seem to whirl around like nebulae; straight bars twist themselves upwards, screw-like, to soar into rows of miniature spires, each winged like a bird; the variety is endless. It is as if an abstract ballet has been solidified for all to enjoy for all time. . . .

Gates under Wren's Library at Trinity College, Cambridge,
by Partridge. 1691–2

(Hills and Saunders, Harrow)

The Miller Memorial Gates at Harrow School. 1929

He was writing, of course, not of the earliest wrought-iron workers such as the man who forged the straps and hinges and ornamentation on the church door at Stillingfleet. Rather, he was writing of the work of the men who succeeded that unknown smith: the men who forged the splendid gates still to be seen at Lincoln and St Albans, Winchester, Salisbury, Canterbury, Chester, Durham, York and the many other cathedrals, abbeys and minsters that are among our noblest and most inspiring memorials to the craftsmanship of masons, carpenters, glaziers and smiths. Many of these are twelfth- and thirteenth-century work: the creation of men who had assimilated the experience and felt the influence of their humbler predecessors and, as it were, began where they had left off.

The relatively simple device, for instance, of the sweeping crescent at the hinge end, from the curved jaws of which the central tongue leapt like a great black flame across the width of the door, gradually became less elaborate. A superb example of this artistic modification can be seen in the Victoria and Albert Museum—perhaps the finest repository of these examples of the blacksmith's craft. You will find there a twelfth-century door which was once in St Albans Abbey (see plate opposite page 68). The original timbers have had to be replaced, but the wrought-iron fittings made by a craftsman eight centuries ago are the original work and for the most part in a fine state of preservation.

Glance at it casually and you will at once be reminded of the straps, crescents and other ironwork of that Stillingfleet church door. The basic principle is obviously the same: two hinges, with straps reaching out across the timbers, designed both to reinforce the hinge and to bond the timbers together. But in that one fundamental the similarity ends. Examine the door in detail and you will quickly recognize the advance both in elaboration and in sheer technique that has been

H

made since the Viking-influenced blacksmith laid down his hammer for the last time at Stillingfleet.

The chief difference lies in the elaboration. While the great crescents of the earlier door have been deliberately reduced to small, beautifully proportioned vertical bars only a few inches high, and split at their terminations to impart a sense of lightness without reducing their strength, the rather crude little ornamental flourishes of the earlier door have been translated into glorious free-flowing scrolls. (The scroll, incidentally, as will be seen later, has always been the most outstanding motif in decorative wrought ironwork.)

The two hinge straps in this door from St Albans Abbey have been shortened so that they cross no more than two-thirds of the door; they have been lightened, too, and skilfully incorporated into the overall design of the door furniture. In order to achieve this end, the artist-craftsman-smith allowed his scrolls to follow a natural upward-outward-downward path, each one feeding the next and imparting to it its own impulses, as twigs and leaves branch out from the mother stem. But he also linked his flowing scrolls, above and beneath each diminished strap, by the insertion of a cluster of beautifully forged 'leaves', set on little iron 'twigs'. This suggests that the smith was influenced by the natural growth of what he saw all about him, and sought to translate this into the iron he heated in his forge and hammered on his anvil.

Indeed, there are certain very familiar growing things—the ivy plant, for instance, the vine, the convolvulus—that almost cry aloud to serve as the blacksmith's inspiration; the twisting and turning and flow of their stems and tendrils, the peeling-off of their leaves and buds: these the black-smith down the centuries has wittingly or unwittingly made use of. It was as natural to him to do this as, for instance, it was natural to him to use the basic form of the fleur-de-lis as an ornamental feature, particularly as terminals to his upright bars. The masons who built the churches and cathedrals often used variants of this same device for their crockets and finials.

In the Middle Ages it was generally the ecclesiastics who were the chief patrons and employers of the smiths. They possessed the means to satisfy their desire to beautify the House of the God whom they served. The timber of the earliest churches was soon replaced by stone, until almost the only woodwork to be seen was that in the main doors, the choir stalls and canopies and seating generally. All else was now stone—and ironwork. There was ironwork on the doors, to provide the strength necessary to support their massive weight, and also to add decoration; but once inside the building, iron to a large extent replaced timber altogether. The rails below the altars, in the chancel, sealing off the side chapels from nave and transept, protecting the holy relics, guarding the stone memorials to the great whose bodies had been buried within the edifice itself: all these were of wrought iron. Gates, rails and grilles were the main output of the blacksmiths employed by the builders of the great churches and cathedrals, abbeys and minsters, and by those who served in them down the centuries.

At this time much of the strongest influence came from France. It came also—somewhat unexpectedly—from the Middle East, as a result of the later Holy Crusades. The supposition is that certain blacksmiths who had accompanied the Crusaders as farriers and armourers had been impressed by the latticework to be seen in some of the paynims' palaces, brought back with them their memories of this intricate ironwork and later incorporated it in their own ecclesiastical work. The pagan and the Christian, the secular and the sacred, as so often, became merged into one. There is an example of this to be seen in the form of a grille protecting a monument to the Duke of Gloucester, believed to be the work of a blacksmith who lived towards the end of the thirteenth century.

It was about this time that the famous grille on the tomb of Queen Eleanor of Castile in Westminster Abbey was forged (see plate opposite page 69). It is not often that we have such information about these early specimens of the blacksmith's craft as we have in this case. We know that it is the work of a Bedfordshire man named Thomas, who took his surname from the town of Leighton Buzzard in that county, and appears in the records as 'Thomas de Leghtone'. He made this beautiful grille—generally acknowledged to be one of the supreme examples of the blacksmith's art in this country—in the year 1294. We know what he was paid for it: thirteen pounds, paid in four instalments, and by agreement covering not only his time but the cost of transporting the grille all the way from Leighton Buzzard to London, and the expenses incurred by himself and his assistants while they installed it in the Abbey. Even though that sum of money was worth vastly more than it is today, some seven centuries later, it still strikes us as pitifully inadequate payment for a creation so nobly beautiful.

Examine this masterpiece in detail. The tomb, its stonework showing marks of the centuries that have passed over it, is surmounted by a great slab of stone divided into seven panels, each with a shield topped by a diminutive curved and pointed arch. Above this, flaring upwards into the shadowed air, is Thomas de Leghtone's wrought-iron grille, extending the full length of the tomb, and some distance beyond at each end.

Like the stonework which it surmounts, it is divided into vertical panels, in this case not seven but eleven. Each panel is filled in with an individual design of scrollwork differing from that in every other panel, but at the same time giving an impression of unity. The scrolls themselves are fashioned from moulded bars, and there seems no limit to the variation that the smith has contrived to impart to them—all the more remarkable in view of the relatively constricted panel areas in which he had to work. One small detail that only the practised eye will notice is that the terminations of the individual scrolls—in the traditional leaf-and-flower patterns—have been so organized and disposed as to conceal the welded joints required for the assembly and installation of the grille. That is the sort of small but important detail that only a first-class blacksmith would think of.

The eleven panels curve upwards and outwards, and are surmounted by an iron rail. From this rail springs a row of twenty-six beautifully proportioned trident-shaped ornaments. These vary slightly one from another, some of them having a thin, tapering middle 'tongue', others a barbed tongue between two thin spiky 'jaws'. At a little distance, and seen against a light background, they are reminiscent of the cactus plants to be found in the Arizona desert. Each, in fact, is a terminal to the series of upright bars separating the panels and dividing the panels down the centre—bars to and from which spring those highly individual specimens of scrollwork which are the glory of de Leghtone's work.

It is possible that these sharp-pointed decorative terminals may have been used as prickets to hold candles burning over the Queen's tomb. Whether or not this is so matters little: the glory of Queen Eleanor's Grille is to be found in the imaginativeness of the overall design and the exquisite variety of its individual details: all forged in a fire-pit and hammered to shape on a thirteenth-century blacksmith's anvil.

The bishops and abbots, however, were not the only patrons and employers of the smiths in the Middle Ages and

later. Though most of the best-preserved specimens of their
work is naturally to be found in the churches and cathedrals,
because there they were protected from the weather and, to
a large extent, from the damage that could be caused to
them by vandals, many examples of this type of wrought
ironwork do exist elsewhere. There are castle gates, for
instance, portcullises and other types; there are railings and
gates that gave (or prevented) access to ornamental gardens
on private estates, when life had become less tempestuous
and the wealthy land-owners could expend their wealth on
leisured living instead of on armaments.

It is perhaps here that the continuity of this tradition in
blacksmithery is easiest to follow, for the blacksmith today
is still called upon to forge ornamental gates and railings
for private estates, for public buildings of many kinds, for
schools and colleges and other institutions. Our older
universities, particularly Oxford and Cambridge, are especially rich in examples of the blacksmith's craft, as re-
vealed in their high railings and huge double gates. Many
of these date back some centuries; others are comparatively
recent installations, the result, perhaps, of some generous
benefaction.

Everyone who has delved into this aspect of blacksmithery knows the names of such men as the Huguenot
refugee Jean Tijou, whose influence on decorative wrought-
iron workers in the seventeenth and eighteenth centuries was
immense and lasting. Another great name, that of a native
this time, is Robert Bakewell, a Derbyshire smith whose
'Birdcage' arbour at Melbourne Hall is justly famous. Two
Welsh blacksmiths, the Davies brothers, were jointly responsible for the magnificent gates at Chirk Castle, near Llangollen, now two hundred and fifty years old but still in a
splendid state of preservation (see plate opposite page 76).

The blacksmiths' names, and the examples of wrought

ironwork associated with them, could be multiplied almost indefinitely, for there was this tremendous upsurge of inspiration in the centuries that followed the coming of the Vikings, the Norman Conquest and the Crusades—each of which produced its specific influence. But it is time now to have a look at the technique of the men who produced these masterpieces of the blacksmiths' craft.

7

Individual skills

Relatively few of the innumerable tools and items of equipment to be found in a smithy are required for shoeing; the majority of them have been evolved for the more general work the smith undertakes. Each has its specific function in the various stages of manipulating the raw material and transforming it into the finished product—whether it is a cottager's broken spade or a pair of gates for the main entrance to his lordship's parkland, costing a thousand pounds or so.

Just as he has recourse to a number of highly specialized tools for these varied jobs, so he must possess a number of individual and highly specialized skills, which he will have perfected during his years of blacksmithing. Some of these are basic: examples of technique as essential to the completion of the job in hand as the carpenter's ability to square-off a piece of wood or the potter's to 'throw' his lump of clay on to his wheel.

Perhaps the foremost of these—even in an age when oxy-acetylene and electric-arc welding are becoming more and more a feature of most types of engineering workshop—is the technique of Fire welding, or Forge welding. Essentially, this is the technique of uniting two pieces of iron by bringing them to exactly the requisite heat and then hammering them together on the anvil. To watch a practised smith doing this is perhaps not altogether fair to him, for he makes it look so easy. In fact it calls for shrewd judgement, both of metals and of what he refers to as heats, and a highly developed sense of timing between anvil and forge. There are, however, two preliminary stages required in most forge welding: Upsetting (also known as Jumping-up) and Scarfing.

Suppose for example that the smith has to fire-weld together two lengths of iron bar of one-inch section. He knows that when the two ends that are to be joined have received the necessary hammering on all four sides they will have been very considerably reduced in thickness, and acquired in the process an unwanted 'waist'. He therefore allows for this by upsetting, or jumping-up, the ends involved in the join. The method he adopts is as follows.

Having brought the iron to the right degree of malleability, he drops it firmly, red-hot end downwards, on to the anvil face—'jumping it up'. He repeats this process several times over, according to the section of the bar. If it is of very large section he may even up-end it on the anvil and proceed to hammer it vertically downwards. But he must be very careful in doing this not to bend the bar. With this in mind, he has probably taken only a very small heat, so that only the last few inches of the bar have become really hot.

Gradually those last few inches of glowing iron thicken and spread outwards, broadest at the base and decreasing upwards to the original thickness. The smith then treats the other piece of iron in exactly the same way. If necessary he returns each length for further heating and then whips it out for further upsetting. It is imperative that the splayed ends of the two bars shall match exactly.

Now, leaving one bar in the fire-pit, he starts on the second process that is preliminary to the actual forge welding; this is called Scarfing. It consists in hammering the swollen end of each bar, over the anvil edge, into a flat, spoon-shaped 'lip'. The two 'lips' will be placed on top of one another and hammered together while at exactly the right heat, thus being fire-welded into one; or, as the smith may put it, being 'married'.

He now calls upon the services of his mate, or striker, for the next stage is a two-man job. Smith and striker take one piece of iron each from the hearth and swing them smartly on to the anvil, their two red-glowing ends at welding heat butted up against one another and very slightly overlapping. Not a split second must be wasted, or too much heat may be lost. The master smith, gripping one piece in his tongs, while the striker holds the other piece in position, raises his hammer and strikes the overlapping ends sufficiently hard to 'tack' them together. The two matching faces bite, and hold. Now it is time for the striker to get to work with the sledge, while the master smith turns the bar on the anvil face this way and that, at the same time interspersing his own light hammer blows till he is satisfied that the weld is perfect.

By now the glow of the iron has dulled, but still the striker continues to swing his sledge, and little by little the bulge where the two lips overlapped is reduced. Another heat is taken, followed by a second bout of hammering; perhaps even a third and a fourth, if the section of the iron is considerable. You will have noticed, incidentally, that throughout the scarfing and forge welding the smith has been continuously on the look out for 'scale'—those little slivers, very often no larger than sequins, that flake off hot iron under the hammer. They must be prevented from slipping between the two faces of the iron that are being married, or a true weld will be impossible. The smith has been continuously tapping the iron lightly with his hammer, and the scale has been spilling off it on to the anvil face and from there, owing to its deliberate slight tilt, on to the smithy floor.

There are refinements to this protracted hammering operation. Though a good smith and his striker in collaboration can reduce a bulge until only an expert's eye could detect where it had been, there are ways of achieving a better 'finish'. These will certainly be adopted if, for instance, the section of the bar is not square but round, hexagonal or some other shape, as so often in ornamental wrought ironwork. Then the interplay of hammers will not produce the required result, so the smith must have recourse to other tools in his armoury.

He lays over the join an appropriately shaped Forming tool—one of his large collection of top and bottom swages. This will have a concave inner face that, when applied to the welded bar and heavily hammered, will restore it to its original section. The smith first drops the bottom half of his forming tool into the hardie hole; then, having taken the appropriate heat once more, he lays the joined part of the bar in it, closes it with the top swage and nods to his striker. He watches keenly while the blows from the sledge on the forming tool reduce the join to the right section and size. It is an operation calling for expert judgement, for the iron is cooling all the time and must not be struck after the safe temperature has been passed.

Upsetting, or jumping-up, is the method of expanding the section of iron bar, whether temporarily for a welding job or permanently for some other reason; Drawing-out, or Drawing-down, is, as the term implies, the way to reduce the section of a bar. It is a less elaborate process than the other, but still one that calls for skill and judgement. It is an operation less often carried out as an end in itself than as a preliminary to some other process. It is particularly important as an early stage in scroll making—itself one of the most beautiful examples of a blacksmith's technique.

Suppose that the blacksmith is going to make a scroll to be

fitted into some piece of ornamental wrought ironwork. He selects the appropriate size of flat-section iron bar—for example, an inch wide by a quarter of an inch thick. Though the main body of the scroll will be this thickness throughout its length, one of its ends—or both ends if he is making a 'C' scroll—must be tapered off to something near a knife-edge. This can only be done by hammering. The bar is first brought to the appropriate heat in the forge. Then he may hammer it direct; or he may lay a top tool such as a flatter upon it while his striker uses the sledge. For heavier-gauge iron bar this would certainly be the chosen method.

Drawing-out lengthens the bar; it necessarily widens it also. The smith thus has the problem of tapering off the metal to the required length and thinness while at the same time retaining its correct width. This involves the varying of his hammer blows in a regularly graduated sequence. The procedure is as follows. He inserts the end of the iron into the hearth to take a near-welding heat. Meanwhile, since no time must be wasted when the correct heat has been attained, his hammer is laid in readiness on the anvil, the handle towards his hand. He turns the iron this way and that in the fire-pit to ensure that it is heated uniformly—a most important factor in the operation.

At the crucial moment he snatches the bar from the fire, lays the red-hot end on the anvil face, picks up his hammer and begins a rhythmic series of hammer blows, comparatively light at the upper end of the heated part but increasing steadily in weight as he comes nearer to the tip. He strikes a succession of blows, perhaps six in all, first on one side and then on the other. These blows not only elongate the strip but widen it, particularly at the lower end where they fall most heavily. So he must deliver them not only on each face in turn but also on the opposing edges, to prevent the iron from spreading unduly.

The process involves taking a succession of heats. After each heat, having made sure that there is no loose scale either on the anvil face or on the iron itself, he hammers methodically until the heat has been lost, the bar growing longer and more tapering all the time, provided he has watched it carefully throughout his hammering; it being hammered back on its edges so that it retains its original width. Eventually there will be a taper of anything from two inches to double or three times that length, according to the overall proportions of the intended scroll; the edges will be square and true, the width correct and uniform, the taper progressive over its full length from the quarter-inch to the knife-edge at the tip.

When he is satisfied that the result is what he aimed at, the smith takes one more heat, a cherry-red this time. This renders the iron sufficiently malleable for him to be able to remove, either with hammer alone or with hammer and flatter, any small irregularities, unevennesses or rough hammer marks left on it during the earlier stages of forging. The blacksmith is as concerned to avoid unnecessary marks of forging on his ironwork as a good joiner is to avoid marks left by a plane or chisel that has a nick in its edge. (An exception to this general rule occurs when it is intended to leave a 'hammered' effect on the surface of the iron, which is usually done with a ball-peen or other special type of hammer.)

The blacksmith now has his straight length of iron, tapered at one end (or both if it is to be a 'C' scroll). But the real work is only just about to begin. He has still to fashion the scroll from the prepared bar. The scroll is unquestionably the most common and at the same time the most graceful and pleasing motif in all ornamental wrought ironwork. The variety of curve and scroll terminal is limitless, and the placing of scrolls in panels and frames offers an inexhaustible challenge to the artist-craftsman. There is evidence of this from the earliest specimens of scroll-decorated ironwork, such as that in the church door at Stillingfleet, right through the Middle Ages to the beautiful examples being forged in such smithies as those of George Lister & Sons, H. B. Bullingham & Son and many others today.

A well-proportioned scroll skilfully incorporated in the overall design of a piece of wrought ironwork—whether gate, fire-screen, inn-sign, balustrade or anything else, large or small—has a quality about it that suggests that it is, somehow, natural; that it is, in fact, the work of Mother Nature herself petrified into iron. It is immediately reminiscent of foliage: foliage seen in its natural, growing or 'flowing' state and captured and held once and for all by the perception, artistry and skill of the smith. A West Country smith who knew as well as any man how to do this has written: 'Particularly happy to the design of wrought ironwork is the scroll, that lovely, vital motif which comes straight from Nature herself. It is the gentlest of all emblems.' No description of a scroll could be simpler or more precise.

When a scroll—whether elaborate or simple—is to be a single specimen, not one of a pair or a series, it will most probably be shaped by eye alone, on the beak and face of the anvil, by hammer blows and nothing else. This calls for very great skill and an eye that is almost magical in its judgement of proportion and curve. The iron is heated a little at a time, starting always at the tapered end that has already been drawn-out and working through the whole length a few inches at a time. The beak of the anvil will have been the guide for the expansion of its progressive curves, for being tapered itself from point to stout base it offers an infinitely varied series of convex surfaces on which to hammer the iron.

More often, however, scrolls appear in the finished piece in panels containing scores. A fine example of this use of scrollwork is to be seen in the exquisite eighteenth-century gate at New College, Oxford (see plate opposite page 77). Both in order to save time and, especially, to ensure uniformity, the scrolls are made on a Scroll-form with the assistance of Scroll-dogs. The scroll-form is exactly what the term implies: a device for forming the scroll. It consists of a massive two-, three-, or four-turn spiral of heavy section iron, with its centre drawn slightly upwards so that it has the appearance of a skeletonized cone. Its base is square-section, turned at right angles to the spiral, very slightly tapered and designed to be dropped into the hardie hole or alternatively to be held in the jaws of the leg-vice. The scroll-dogs, or scroll-wrenches, consist of a pair of angled tongs, or two stubs at right angles to an iron bar and an inch or so apart. These are used to apply the iron to the scroll-form during the operation.

The smith starts at the tapered end of the prepared iron. He has already measured and cut it to the right length, and will by now have brought the last few inches to a red heat. Now he whips it out of the hearth and lays it across the anvil, with half an inch or so of the flowing end projecting over the far edge. This he taps lightly downward with a calculated blow of his hand-hammer. Then he turns the bar over so that its angled tip is pointing upwards, and lightly taps it from the far side in such a way that the tip folds over on itself and now forms a small hook.

He re-heats the iron, taking a somewhat larger heat than before so that when he removes the bar it is glowing along much of its length. It is ready now for the next stage. He drops the bar over the scroll-form in such a way that the hooked tip he has just forged engages with the uppermost, closely curved terminal of the scroll-form. Immediately it is engaged he proceeds to move the bar clockwise round the scroll-form, so that it forms a succession of tangents to the increasing curve of the spiral. The bar is gripped throughout the operation by the angled tongs or the scroll-dog in such a

way that it is forced close up against the continuous curve.
If the heat is right and he moves swiftly, the smith may be
able to complete the scroll without returning it to the fire;
when making large scrolls, however, he may have to re-heat
the bar a second or even a third or fourth time, further and
further along its length, and so complete the scroll in two or
more 'takes'.

Though he makes the scroll single-handed, the process is a
good example of a two-handed job. Holding the end of the
bar in his left hand, with or without tongs according to its
length, he swings it round the scroll-form; meanwhile, with
his scroll-dog he 'nips' the hot iron firmly against the cold
iron of the scroll-form at intervals of a few inches at a time, to
ensure that it is taking the right curve uniformly throughout
—a curve which, of course, has a continuously expanding
radius—as he comes nearer and nearer to the final curve
of the spiral. To watch an expert scroll maker at work is to
realize how successfully two hands can perform two entirely
different motions continuously, co-ordinated by one pair of
eyes and one brain. The scroll that results from this combined operation is itself an object of beauty that gives the
impression of having 'flowed' into the shape that it has
finally assumed.

Quite apart from their differing sizes, scrolls take a variety
of shapes. They may be simple scrolls, such as may be seen
in the traditional type of shepherd's crook—and there are
still one or two smithies specializing in this work. They may
be double scrolls, taking either the form of a capital-letter
'C' or that of a capital 'S'. They may flow into one another,
curving outwards and away and then back towards one
another as though reluctant to remain permanently separated. But they possess always this essential quality of 'alive-
ness'; and having that quality, they impart a sense of movement to the rigid verticals and horizontals of the framework

Ribbon-end

Fishtail

Snub-end

into which they are ordinarily fitted.

They vary, too, in the way in which the central and smallest curve of the scroll, or terminal, is finished off. These varying patterns, traditional and, many of them, as old as the craft itself, bear names that are often picturesque, and evocative. 'Ribbon-end', for instance; 'Leaf-end', 'Fishtail', 'Snub-end', 'Bolt-end', 'Halfpenny' and 'Blow-over-leaf'. Sometimes there is a combination of the terms: 'Fishtail-snub-end', or 'Halfpenny Snub-end', for example. These scroll-ends, as may be imagined, vary also a good deal in the demands they make on the skill and patience of the scroll maker.

The simplest and most ordinary is the ribbon-end. For this, the iron of which the scroll is made is simply hammered out to a taper that approximates to a knife edge. It may also be slightly narrower than the main body of the scroll,

Fishtail-Snub-end

Halfpenny Snub-end

Leaf-end

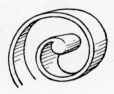

Bolt-end

Scrolls

and usually has slightly rounded corners. Exactly the reverse of this is the fishtail. Here, though the metal is drawn out to a fine taper the last half-inch or so is hammered with sufficient force to 'spread' the metal. It thus acquires the appearance of a small fan or, as the name aptly suggests, a fish's tail.

The snub-end scroll is slightly more elaborate. Instead of being hammered out thin, as in the fishtail and the ribbon-end, the tip is laid over the far edge of the anvil and hammered in such a way as to 'bunch-up' the metal into a little knob. Behind the knob the iron is drawn-down by judicious hammering in such a way that the 'snub' is emphasized. Then the snub has to be 'dressed'. The smith hammers it with a succession of expertly applied light blows until it acquires the proportions of a miniature billet, or bolster. It is really as though a wafer-thin scroll-end had been hammered repeatedly into itself, to form this tiny cylinder that now lies athwart the line of the scroll.

The smith may well not be content with a mere snub-end; he may decide to develop it into a fishtail-snub-end, or, as he may refer to it, a 'fishtail-knib'. In order to produce this most pleasing form of scroll terminal he first splits the tapered end so as to allow it to expand rather more than it would otherwise do. Then he rolls up the spread ends upon themselves, in such a way that they expand slightly on the two outer edges. When the resulting cylinder has set solid he has produced a delicately curved miniature scroll on each side of the snub-end of the main scroll to which it serves as terminal.

The scrolls described so far—and many other variants— are all of ribbon metal, rectangular in section. But the expert smith, called upon to produce something out of the ordinary, will work with iron bar of quite different section; or he will impart a twist to the bar as he forges it into a scroll; or he will bevel it in such a way that it is corkscrewing, so to speak, in two distinct planes. If he is working on a pattern inspired by foliage he will instinctively follow its familiar curves (see plate opposite page 96), so that his iron takes on the flowing movement of tendrils and the terminals of his scrolls may be leaves—perhaps hollow, or curving over and away from the plane of the panel into which they are fitted.

When he is forging this more elaborate type of scroll the smith cannot make use of his scroll-form. He obtains his results solely by the skilful use of hammers and swages on the face and beak of his anvil. It is not greatly exaggerating to say that in such work he has virtually turned sculptor in iron and is producing something that bears comparison with the masterpieces of men who work in stone. An example of such a masterpiece is to be seen in the Victoria and Albert Museum; it is a panel from a staircase formerly at Lincoln's Inn Fields, in London.

There is really no limit to the possible variations of these curves. The expert smith can respond to the demands made upon him with astonishing readiness. Indeed, his skill has something uncanny, almost of magic, in it: for he is working in iron that has to be brought to an exact heat, struck with the appropriate hammers at the critical angle and the requisite strength, twisted with the right scroll-dogs or wrenches in the few seconds that elapse before the vital heat is dispersed, and all the time shaped to measurements carried in his eye; even if he has the assistance of a scroll-form for part of the operation it is an object that he will first have designed and forged himself for the very job in hand. It is small wonder that the man who works in iron retains even to this day something of the aura of mystery which has enshrouded him since the far-off days of Hephaestus, Vulcan, Wayland and their fellow-smiths.

*　　　　*　　　　*　　　　*

Scrolls rarely appear singly in any piece of ornamental wrought ironwork; they are usually incorporated in pairs or in series, balancing scrolls reversed against them in adjacent panels. They may be disposed between the verticals of a gate or grille or balustrade, for instance; or there may be no such interposed rails and their outer curves will thus be in immediate contact with the corresponding curves of their opposite numbers. In any case they need to be fitted into and attached to the ironwork of which they form an integral part. This can be done in a variety of ways.

The simplest way is to weld the juxtaposed portions. This may be done by oxy-acetylene or electric-arc welding; obviously it cannot be done by fire welding, for the simple reason that this would involve placing both portions of the ironwork in the fire-pit to take a welding heat, and this would hardly be practicable. Many smiths prefer welding to any other method, and not merely because it is both the quickest and the cheapest. The great merit of welding is that if it is expertly done there is no interruption to the flowing line of the scroll; it is often impossible to detect the exact spot where the weld fused scroll and bar or scroll and scroll together. But there are other smiths, no less practised, who prefer one or other of the alternative methods; methods that were in vogue during the golden age of large-scale ornamental ironworking, when the Church employed the smith, and have been favoured ever since.

One of these alternative methods is pinning, or riveting: the terms are self-explanatory. Holes of a suitable size, the smaller within reason the better, are hot-punched or cold-drilled in the two pieces of iron, whether scroll and scroll or scroll and bar, the two holes are matched and an iron pin, or rivet, passed through and hammered over at each end to lock the two faces together. If the ends of the rivet are skilfully hammered down, perhaps even lightly touched with the file, then there is little more 'bulge' than is the case when the welding method has been adopted. It does, however, take more time and it certainly demands a very high degree of judgement, for the related holes must be marked and punched in advance so that when the two pieces of iron— perhaps both on different curves—are brought together the two holes exactly correspond. One sign of second-rate work is when the rivet has been driven through the metal at a point fractionally removed from the true point of contact, so that slight distortion results.

A third method, and one much preferred by many first-class ornamental smiths, is the use of the Collar, or Clip. This, too, is a self-explanatory term. The clip is a small piece of iron, a quarter of an inch or more in width and an eighth of an inch or so in thickness, so shaped that when heated it can be passed right round the point of union. It quickly cools down, shrinking as it cools. As it shrinks it exerts a vice-like grip on the two pieces of iron, bonding them together as surely as if they had been welded.

If there is an objection to this method, other than the fact that making and fitting clips demands a good deal of time and so adds considerably to the cost of the job, it is that clips do tend to break the flowing line of the scrollwork, for many people its chief attraction. On the other hand, if there are a great many of these clips, all identical in size and symmetrically disposed throughout the whole area of scrollwork, then they may be said actually to enhance the overall effect; the subtle and variegated curves are there, accentuated by the trim, unobtrusive clips.

Clip-making, therefore, is one of the blacksmith's individual skills. It is a fascinating operation to watch, for the pieces of iron he is working with are so small that it seems impossible that with anything so massive as hammer and anvil he can forge anything so diminutive. But he can, and does, and with remarkable speed and accuracy. I have watched a Kentish blacksmith turning out these miniature clips in rapid succession for an hour on end, to be fitted later on a series of wrought-iron door-knockers he had made the previous day.

His raw material was iron bar, or rod, a quarter of an inch wide by three-sixteenths of an inch thick. In the hardie hole of his anvil there lay a type of swage which was in effect two square-section bars welded parallel to a base-plate about half an inch apart. Having heated the last three inches of his bar, he whipped it out of the hearth, cut off the glowing end with a hot set, laid this across his swage and, holding a squared piece of iron across the 'bridge' thus formed, struck it sharply once, and once only. The heated bar was thus forced down into the gully between the bars of the swage; its two ends rose up proportionately. Holding it in his tongs, he then turned it over and struck it again, once on each side. The result was a rectangular 'ring' rather less than an inch in length, perhaps a quarter of an inch in internal measurement and with one unjoined side.

The next stage was to fit the clip. He placed it in the hearth to take the appropriate heat, then whipped it out with his tongs, slipped it over the two pieces of metal to be joined, and while it was still glowing cherry-red gave it a series of smart blows, not too heavy and not too light but just sufficient to make the two ends forming the open side bond together. The clip cooled rapidly; and as it did so it shrank on the metal it enclosed with a grip powerful enough to hold it in place for ever.

To complete the operation the smith tapped the clip on all four sides with feather-light touches of his hammer; as a result, it took on the attractive quality of hammered, or 'beaten', iron that matched the knocker itself. A lesser smith might not have bothered with this small refinement; but it is a fact that those final touches made quite a difference to the completed job: the clip had been made an integral part of the whole assembly. That smith is the son of a blacksmith, and the grandson of a blacksmith; all three smiths are working today, in smithies in three different counties, the youngest of them twenty-five years old, the eldest eighty-two.

*   *   *   *

Another characteristic feature of wrought ironwork, whether in small articles like candlesticks and fire-irons or in gates and grilles, is the twisted bar. As a decorative feature it ranks second only to the scroll. To produce it, almost invariably from square-section bar, calls for a highly specialized technique and, as always in the smithy, the use of keen judgement. This is especially so when the twist is to be imparted not to the whole of the bar but only to certain sections of it.

The simplest form of twisted bar is made from a single piece of square-section iron. Provided it is not more than half an inch thick the twist can be put into it 'cold'. One end of the bar is gripped in the jaws of a vice; the other end is held in the centre of a two-handed wrench consisting of a stout iron bar hammered flat midway along its length and punched with a square, tapered hole. The smith gives the wrench a succession of vigorous half-turns, counter-clockwise for a right-hand twist, clockwise for a left-hand one, until he obtains the degree and length of twist he requires. Provided his leverage on the wrench is constant the twist produced will be uniform throughout the whole length of the bar.

If the section of the bar to be twisted is greater than half an inch—and this is often the case when he is forging gates and grilles and balustrades—then the bar must be twisted 'hot'. Now, of course, complications arise. It is obvious, for example, that a bar twists most readily where it is softest; that is to say, where it has been brought to the greatest heat. The blacksmith has therefore to make sure that the whole of the length to be twisted has been brought to a uniform heat, and this necessitates a much larger fire than he ordinarily uses. He may even use sheet-iron panels to construct a special type of 'long fire'. In any case he must bring his bar to a uniform bright red heat throughout the whole of the length to be twisted.

Another problem, particularly with a longish bar, is to prevent it from sagging under its own weight while being twisted, for a bar is always worked horizontally. His ingenious answer to this problem is to slip over and along the heated bar what he calls a Barrel: a length of iron tubing of rather larger diameter than the bar itself. This keeps it almost perfectly straight, and he can correct any minor deviations from the true by manipulation in the vice when the bar has cooled.

Some of the finest examples of this element in wrought ironwork are to be seen at Hampton Court Palace, and there are others no less outstanding in the notable collection of such work at the Victoria and Albert Museum. A small but particularly beautiful example of twisted wrought ironwork there is a seven-foot-long church chandelier rod, with fittings, the work of a seventeenth-century smith (see plate opposite page 97). On a larger scale there are the great twisted bars in the gate of Bishop West's Chapel in Ely Cathedral. To examine such work is to recognize and appreciate the inventive skill of the blacksmiths who, down the ages, have so ingeniously solved their many problems.

It may happen that the design of the wrought ironwork the smith has been commissioned to forge requires that the bar shall be alternately straight and twisted—perhaps in the proportion of six or eight inches of twist between each two-foot run of straight. This means that the smith must keep part of his bar cold while the adjacent section is brought to the requisite bright red heat. To make sure that his alternating lengths of hot and cold conform to the specifications laid down he will make frequent use of his bosh. In it he will quench any part of the bar that has become heated when it should not have done, and then quickly impart the required twist to the still-glowing section.

Square bars are the basic raw material of twisted wrought ironwork, but they are by no means the only bars used. Examine any of the outstanding examples of decorative ironwork and you will soon see that there are twisted bars in them that were never of square section even to begin with. There are ornamental twists suggesting that a number of thin bars, or rods, have been 'plaited' together, or twisted like rope. And this, in fact, is the case. The smith has taken, say, two bars a quarter of an inch square and two bars of the same thickness but round; or he may have taken two thin square rods and two thin ribbon bars; or two rounds and one ribbon; or indeed any one of a number of possible variations. These he will have twisted together, at bright red heat, so that they have fused, while at the same time retaining a hint of their individual section. The resultant bar is known as a 'composite'; but that is a drab name indeed for an ornate bar resembling perhaps the stem of some plant round which the tendrils of some smaller plant—ivy, for instance, or convolvulus—have wound their spiralling way.

The individual rods must always be welded together at each end (as a rope must be 'whipped'); but it is not necessary to fuse them along the whole of their length, for they will not 'unwind'. If the proportions are right, and the degree of twist imparted to them is uniform, then they will maintain contact throughout their length, giving the impression of being one ornate whole without having lost anything of their original identity. In certain cases the black-smith may in fact wish to ensure that they are not closely united except at each end. He may have decided, for instance, to form the upper end of each of his bars into a 'hollow twist'. This is often the shape forming the handles of a set of fire-irons. It is a lovely shape to look at, and a pleasing one to feel in the hand. How, in fact, does he produce it?

He first takes four (or three or five) short lengths of, say, eighth-inch round or square-section iron rod and fire-welds them to the end of the stouter square or round bar that is to be the stem of the article—say a poker. He next welds the unattached, or 'loose', ends of the short rods. They are now fused together at each end. Then he puts one end in the vice, grips the other with his wrench, and twists them as though he were twisting a solid bar. Since their section is small he can do this 'cold'. Having done this, he then inserts the twisted end in his fire, brings it to the necessary heat, and then proceeds to reverse the twist half a turn or so. This process opens out the small rods spirally, so that they bulge in the middle and provide the required hollow, and inciden-tally heat-insulating, grip.

*   *   *   *

It would, of course, be possible to go on for a very long time describing the various individual techniques of which the smith specializing in decorative wrought ironwork must make himself master; scrolls, twisted bars, 'wavy' bars—another self-explanatory term—are simply a handful of them. To study a fine set of gates, or some other piece of wrought ironwork on the large scale, is to realize that there is practically no end to the variants in the manipulation of iron which can be demonstrated.

Take for example one of the many gates at Trinity

College, Cambridge (see plate opposite page 112). This is a college gate set within an enclosing grille, the work of an English smith named Partridge who flourished in the last years of the seventeenth century. It is really a double gate, and one of a group which are beneath Wren's Library at the College and were built in 1691–2. Each of the gates is identical and consists of eight sturdy uprights, the two outermost of which are technically known as Rails. The overall frame, of course, is rectangular; but it is so skilfully filled in with a variety of scrollwork, wavy bars and other forms of ornamentation that the plain rigid rectangle is not over-emphasized.

Between the bottom and the first rail there is no ornamentation; between the first and second rails the verticals are separated one from the other each by an inverted 'C' scroll, from the middle of which there projects downwards a spike in the form of a short wavy bar like a flickering lizard's tongue.

The main ornamentation is to be found in the second and top panels of the gates, and continued outwards to left and right across the grille of which the gates form the centre section. It consists of a supremely lovely juxtaposition of scrolls that fill the angles and contain other and smaller panels of combined scrollwork and other ornamental devices. You will find a notably rich variety of scroll-ends, with delicate leaf-ends on variously moulded bars. Looking at them closely, it is easy to discover what particular leaves were the master-smith's chief inspiration here. The other 'empty' panel is characterized by 'C' scrolls with the flickering tongue; and there is a further row of these, pointing upwards, along the full length of the top rail spanning the width of the grille.

It was a much more modern smith who designed and forged the gates for the Bill Yard at Harrow School known as the Miller Memorial Gates (see plate opposite page 113) in 1929: the West Country smith who has already been referred to and quoted. His gates are double gates: a pair of wrought-iron gates set between massive brick pillars and surmounted by what is technically known as an Overthrow. The chief beauty of this pair of gates lies, I think, in the contrast between the simplicity, amounting almost to austerity, of the design of the actual gates and the elaborate ornamentation of this surmounting feature.

An overthrow is the decorative ironwork that spans the whole width between the two gateposts and usually remains fixed while the gates swing beneath it. In certain instances, however, when there is the likelihood of a high load having to enter, the overthrow itself is hinged at one or both ends, so that it can at need be swung open independently of the gates. Originally an overthrow was designed as an integral part of the gates, and made therefore in two halves. But because its elaborate ornamentation put too much strain on the gate hinges in due course it was 'lifted' from the top rails and made independent of them. It then served the additional purpose of a stay pressing outwards against the supporting piers or pillars, and helped thus to counteract the weight of the gates themselves. Once this principle had been accepted the artist-craftsman responsible for the gates could indulge as he liked in the elaboration of the ornamental ironwork.

This particular pair of gates at Harrow School has, in each gate, two main stiles, with seven verticals between them, a bottom rail, a twofold rail one-third of the way up, and an exquisitely proportioned curved top rail rising from just above the upper hinge to the uppermost point of the gate, just beneath the lower curve of the overthrow, which corresponds to it exactly. Between the bottom rail and the twofold one some eighteen inches higher up there is inserted between each vertical and its neighbour a short bar known as a Dog-bar. This, as the term suggests, is a fill-in designed to prevent dogs from passing between the main bars. These dog-bars are often topped by short, sharp spikes, fleurs-de-lis, wavy tongues, arrow-heads or barbs, designed to prevent intruders from using the lower rail as a step by which to climb over the gate when it is locked. The dog-bars, incidentally, give a little extra visual 'weight' to the base, thus improving the overall proportions.

But this West Country smith has produced a variant on the basic principle of the dog-bar. Instead of fitting it straight from the bottom rail to the next rail up, he has broken the line by inserting in his double cross-rail a row of eighteen iron rings each set within an enclosing square; above these the interrupted dog-bars terminate in wavy spikes. The effect is at once delicate and strong, utilitarian and artistic. It is in details such as this that the first-class smith can be distinguished from his lesser brethren.

It is in the overthrow, and also in the tall, narrow panels between the brick piers and the hinged stiles, that the real ornamentation of this set of gates at Harrow School is to be found. This West Country smith has strong views on the making of scrolls.

At the Devon Smithy [he wrote] we bend all our scrolls by sight, resting the iron on the beak of the anvil and tapping it into the proper shape with a hammer, bit by bit. This is a tricky business, and not every iron-worker can make scrolls this way. But it produces excellent results, with the great advantage that each scroll is separately made and is therefore quite unique.

The truth of his contention can be seen by close examination of any of his scrollwork, at Harrow School, at Buckfast Abbey in his own county, at Dunster Castle not far away, at Lincoln College, Oxford, and elsewhere. All his work has that hallmark, that 'signature', that characterizes the products of the true master smith, the combination of his many individual skills.

8

'The gate hangs well'

W HEN next you examine leisurely a gate such as one of those already described, consider for a moment what may be called its birth, or inception. For you are, after all, looking at the finished article: the product of an artist's imagination and the blacksmith's traditional craftsmanship. The artist—sometimes an architect—will have designed the gate to blend with the general design of the building to which it is to be, as it were, an introduction; the craftsman (who in some cases, as in that of the Devon smith, is the same man) will have had to translate the drawing from a series of lines on paper to a three-dimensional object of wrought iron. How, then, does he set about this translation?

A conspicuous feature of any smithy in which large-scale wrought-iron objects are forged is a low-set table. It is no ordinary table, however. It is a solidly constructed rectangular iron framework perhaps ten or twelve feet long by six or eight feet wide, firmly rooted to the smithy floor, well lit from above, large enough to serve as a 'bed' for a really substantial piece of wrought ironwork, such as a carriageway gate or a length of balustrade.

The framework supports a dead-flat surface of sheet iron; this may be no more than an eighth of an inch in thickness, but it will be so uniformly braced and supported from beneath that it has almost a billiard-table surface. This high degree of alignment is absolutely essential. For if a gate is not kept accurately in one plane throughout all stages of its construction it will at some point or other develop 'sway', or 'wind', or 'twist', and from that moment onwards it will be virtually impossible to restore it to perfect straightness either vertically or horizontally. In a sense the blacksmith is confronted with the same problem as the joiner: 'warp', or 'wind', in their raw material—whether timber or iron—is the bane of both their lives.

So, the smithy table is erected with the most meticulous attention to its levels; so far as is practicable it is carefully preserved from the risk of damage from the impact of heavy objects being dropped upon it, and it is constantly checked with spirit-level and straight-edge to ensure that its uniformity of surface is maintained. Uniformity of surface; but not, as might be expected, smoothness. In fact the sheet iron forming the table-top is rusted all over. There is a definite reason for this, and it becomes clear in the earliest stages of gate construction, long before that of assembly has been reached. For the smithy table is also the smith's drawing-board.

He works, of course, from an artist's drawing in the first place. This drawing is not scaled down but full-size, and contains a wealth of notes about the precise measurements from point to point, the lengths of bars of various sections, the radii of scrolls and other curved features, the interior and exterior angles, the placement of rivets, collars and welding points, and much else. All this has to be transferred to the table-top before the smith can begin work, for he will have to lay out his bars and scrolls in accordance with the artist's specifications.

It is obvious that he cannot simply lay the hot metal on top of the drawing he is to work from, for at the first contact the paper would burst into flames and be destroyed. Instead, he must embark upon a process that is complicated at first sight, though in fact extremely effective: a process of transfer.

He first takes a large sheet of brown paper, lays it on the table-top and sprinkles it liberally and uniformly with finely grated chalk. He then rubs over the chalk with his finger-tips. Next he blows away any chalk that is still loose on the paper, after which he turns the sheet of paper upside down on the table. He then lays the artist's drawing on top of the paper and proceeds to outline it with a blunt pencil point or the equivalent. The weight of this impresses the chalk on the surface of the sheet iron. When he removes the brown paper he finds a perfect impression, in white lines on rusty black, of the original drawing, down to the last small detail, in reverse. It can be seen now why he favours a slightly rusty surface: this 'takes' the chalk as it is transferred downwards from the paper, whereas a smoother surface would not do so.

Looking down upon the table-top, the smith now sees a white-chalk gate silhouetted on a black background. It is something like a photographic negative, in which black and white are reversed. Like the photographer, he has now to produce a 'positive' from his 'negative'; this will be the wrought-iron gate.

The gate, of course, is constructed piecemeal. That is to say, working from the specifications attached to the drawing, he must forge one at a time his stiles and rails, which constitute the main framework; the variously proportioned panels that are to be the in-fillers of the framework; the scrolls, wavy bars and ornamental devices such as fleurs-de-lis, conventional and natural leaves, 'water-leaves', 'hart's-tongue ferns' and the many other individual decorative features that may be required to compose the wrought-iron 'picture'. Every individual piece, small or large, must be forged and fashioned to fit the prescribed proportions of the gate and so contribute to the finished article. In a large gate or grille there will be scores, perhaps even hundreds, of these individual pieces; and they have all in due course to be fitted together. This is the stage at which the gate is to be 'assembled', it is the stage at which for the second time the smithy table comes into its own.

We take it that the individual components have been forged to specification. Now the smith assembles the main framework. This, in every gate, whether large or small, consists of the front and back stiles, or Toe Bar and Back Bar, and the top and bottom rails, or Heel Bars, together with one or more intermediate rails. These have not only been cut to the prescribed length but the stiles have been drilled or slotted at the appropriate points to receive the tenons, or Spills, of the rails, and the rails have been drilled or punched to take the secondary verticals that run through them from bottom to top of the gate, and the shorter dog-bars that fill the space between the bottom and the first intermediate rail. All these iron bars, whatever their length or section, will of course have been tested for straightness in the process of forging. But the smith is not content with a rough check, for in a gate it is vital to have every component perfectly aligned and true. He therefore carries out a second, and more elaborate, form of check.

For this he uses a device which works on the principle of the gunsight. He puts each bar in turn horizontally in his leg-vice and lays across it, as far apart as possible, two short lengths of inverted 'T'-bar into the upper edges of which has been cut a 'V'-notch similar to the back-sight of a rifle. Looking along the bar, he hopes to find the two sights in line. If the two 'T'-bars lying across it are not parallel, if, that is to say, one or other of them is slightly cocked upwards in relation to the other, then the two notches will not coincide and he will know that there is a twist in his bar. He rectifies this by fitting a square-socketed wrench over the end of the bar and bringing pressure to bear upon it in the

K

reverse direction to the twist. The result is its elimination.
As for the matter of straightness of the bar, this is a simpler
process altogether: he lays the bar on his anvil and, with a
blow or two shrewdly judged, brings it into perfect alignment from end to end.

Now he takes his two stiles and two rails and sets them out
on his smithy table. Like a joiner assembling a window-
frame, he taps the tenons at each end of the rails into the
slots in the two stiles. They are, as he knew they would be, a
smooth, exact fit. But at this stage he is not going to lock
them together finally, for there are the intermediate bars to
be incorporated first. So, having satisfied himself as to their
fit, he opens up the four main members of the frame once
more and then reaches for one of the secondary verticals,
of which there may be a dozen, two dozen, or more, so
spaced out as to produce the desired effect of symmetry and
balance. He tests the first one for length, always measured
between tenon 'shoulders' at each end, to make sure that the
bar will fit exactly between top and bottom rails without
distortion. This done, and any small adjustment called for
seen to, he proceeds to match the remaining uprights with
the first one.

The next step in the assembling of the parts may seem a
retrograde one, for he appears to be dismantling the gate
before it is even completed. He removes the two stiles altogether, retaining just the top and bottom rails and the intermediate ones. These have previously been punched or drilled
to take verticals, and it is to the tricky task of fitting these
that he now turns his attention.

Each vertical must first be threaded through the intermediate rails, and this will only be practicable if the bar has
been very carefully prepared; if it is too thick it will not pass
through the rail at all; if it is too thin, even by the thickness
of a wafer, it will be that much loose and the gate as a

result will lack the rigidity that the criss-crossing of rails and
verticals is designed to impart to it. However, the smith has
borne this important factor in mind and all his verticals pass
smoothly, one by one, through the holes in the intermediate
rails under the calculated impact of his hammer.

To avoid 'burring' the edges of the tenons the smith makes
use of what is oddly called a Monkey-tool, or a Holding-up
Dolly, a device specially designed to protect carefully cut
angles from the weight of a hammer. It consists of a collar-
like piece of iron with a hole drilled in it large enough to take
the tenon comfortably. The monkey-tool is slipped over the
tenon and down on to the squared 'shoulder' of the end to be
driven; it thus takes the impact of the hammer, conveys it to
the bar, but at the same time preserves both tenon and shoulder
from damage. A smith keeps a selection of these monkey-tools
by him so that he always has one to fit any job in hand.

Now the tenons themselves can be fitted into the slots
prepared for them in the top and bottom rails. The resulting
framework at this stage resembles a rather elaborate TV
aerial. But the smith is already reaching out across the table-
top for the two stiles. He lays these at right angles to the rails
and for the second time the tenons at the ends of the rails are
driven into their slots. The result is now a rectangular framework of four main bars filled in with one or more intermediate
horizontal rails and a dozen or a score of verticals, some of
them running the full height of the gate, others, being dog-
bars, only filling in the spaces between the bottom and the
first of the intermediate rails. The framework as a whole consists
of a number of tall, narrow panels, some or all of which have
yet to be filled in with the various ornamental devices—the
scrolls, fleurs-de-lis and so forth—that have been specified in
the artist's design and forged in advance by the smith.

But first the smith will want to make sure that the framework (which has yet to be finally 'locked together') is per-

fectly square, and also free from 'wind': that is to say, absolutely in one plane. To check for squareness he is not content
simply to apply a set square to the four corners, for in anything as large as a gate such a method of checking, however
accurate the instrument used, would be less than adequate.
Instead, he uses a measuring-rod. This he lays diagonally
across his gate, first from one bottom corner and then from
the other. This method is at once simpler than the other,
and more accurate. If the measuring-rod shows the two
diagonals to be identical, then he is satisfied.

As a matter of fact this last statement is not strictly true.
The length of one diagonal should *not* be identical with that
of the other; but the difference between them is a deliberate
and carefully calculated one. This calls for some explanation,
since it appears at first to be a contradiction of a point already
strongly emphasized.

However well it is designed and constructed, a gate almost
invariably 'drops' a little on the side away from the hinge.
Because of this known fact, heavy wooden field gates, garage,
workshop and stable doors always carry one or more
diagonal bracing timbers that slant upwards from the lower
end of the hinged stile. This is to counteract the natural
tendency of a wide gate or door to sag under its own weight.

A wrought-iron gate, however, designed to be a thing of
beauty as well as to serve a purpose, very rarely has any
diagonal bars in its composition. It is essentially an assembly
of verticals and horizontals, suitably filled in with decorative
pieces. The smith therefore cannot avail himself of the purely
functional diagonal brace; he must simply accept the fact
that once his gate is hung it will almost certainly begin to sag.
The degree of sag will vary according to the skill and care he
has lavished on its construction and the quality of the
materials he has used.

In view of this he quite deliberately constructs his gate so

that the length of a diagonal drawn from the top of the hinged
stile to the bottom of the front stile will be slightly *less* than
that of the opposite diagonal. The difference in length is
based on his past experience of gate-making. In general, a
gate will 'drop' about one-sixteenth of an inch for every foot
of its width. That is to say, a gate five feet wide between stile
and stile will drop five-sixteenths of an inch, or just over a
quarter of an inch in all. The smith therefore assembles his
gate in such a way that it is fractionally 'out of square'. As
it lies on his table there is of course no strain upon it whatsoever, and his measuring-rod shows him that there is this small
divergence between the lengths of the two diagonals; but
when he 'hangs' the gate and its dead weight begins to tell,
the drop of the front stile will be exactly what he calculated,
and the finished gate will hang square and true.

*   *   *   *

But there is, of course, a great deal to be done to the gate
before the time arrives to hang it. The framework has been
assembled and tested, but there is still the ornamental work
to be incorporated in it. This lengthy process can result in
distortion, so for the time being the smith refrains from
making the tenons fast and contents himself with temporarily 'locking' the main frame within a series of iron cramps,
much as the joiner does when he is waiting for a glued joint
to set. He has a considerable number of these cramps, many
of them made by himself, ranging from little curved bars
not much larger than handcuffs to long bars with sliding
jaws and vice-like grips to lock whole frames together.

He then turns to the fitting of the scrolls, since these are
usually the most numerous of the ornamental components.
He has forged them in advance and they will all be, to within
a fraction of an inch, exactly right in their dimensions and

proportions. However, they are hand-made, not mass-produced, so there may have to be some last-minute manipulation. Though he may be temped to force the scrolls in 'cold'—'springing' them in, as it is termed—a conscientious smith will not do this, for he knows that a scroll which has been forced into position exerts a sideways pressure out of all proportion to its size. If several such scrolls were to be inserted into a panel they could severely distort the whole framework by sheer cumulative pressure.

He therefore makes any final adjustments that may be individually necessary; each scroll can then be slipped into place with only sufficient 'squeeze' to hold it there while he marks out, first with a piece of chalk and then with his centre-punch, the exact spot at which the unions—whether rivets or clips—are to be effected. When the points have been marked the holes have to be drilled; this means that the entire framework has to be dismantled yet again. It can be seen now why the smith did not lock his tenons once and for all when he first assembled it.

The drilling of these holes calls for great care and precision, and can never be done quickly. It is for this reason that the fitting of decorative components into gate panels is so often done these days by oxy-acetylene or electric-arc welding: a touch of the flame at the right temperature and spot, and the metals are immediately fused. In a cheap gate, or any gate where expenditure has to be kept to a minimum, this quick, efficient and easy method of joining scroll to bar or scroll to scroll is usually adopted.

But the true craftsman prefers to follow a tradition established long before any form of welding other than fire welding was known to blacksmiths. He uses rivets or screws with countersunk heads; or he uses clips; sometimes he uses both in conjunction. Examine a well-made gate closely, looking this time particularly for the small details of assembly; visualize as you do so the problems that confronted the craftsman and imagine to yourself the satisfaction he will have derived from solving them by the exercise of his individual skills.

To the casual and uninformed eye any one piece of wrought ironwork looks much the same as any other, save in its general design and overall appearance. It may be a pair of gates, a grille, a weather-vane, a chandelier, a set of fire-irons or log-bars, a standard lamp or ornamental letter-rack, an elaborate bracket supporting an inn-sign—anything, large or small; but quite apart from its design and function there is this detail work. To many connoisseurs, professional or amateur, it is in this detail work that the chief pleasure of examining wrought ironwork is to be found.

Take, as one small example, the 'finish' of the rivets. Nothing, surely, could appear less interesting, less individual, than a rivet. It is simply a small, cylindrical pin, blunt at one end and with a smallish head at the other. It may be technically known as a Snap-head or Countersunk Head. In either case (save in very large riveting jobs such as boiler making, which are not wrought ironwork anyway) it is both driven in and finished off 'cold'. The hole is drilled to the diameter of the rivet, so that close contact is made throughout. The head protrudes at one end and the blunt tip at the other. But it is in the finishing-off of the riveting that the individual style of the smith is to be detected.

The snap-head rivet has a head that is hemispherical, while the other type has a flat head countersunk into a tapered recess in the bar so that it is flush with the surface. But whichever type of rivet is used, it is the blunt tip that is dealt with first. The smith uses a ball-peen hammer of suitable weight. With the head of the rivet firmly held against the anvil, or on the face of a sledge held by the striker, the smith hammers the protruding tip in such a way as to 'spread' it round the lip of the hole through which it has passed. This locks the two (or more) pieces of iron irrevocably together.

It is surprising, though, how many different ways there are of finishing off a rivet; and it is in this, too, that a smith can show his individuality. The rivet, made of mild steel, is tough enough to fulfil its important function but at the same time malleable enough to be shaped 'cold'. By the time the smith's hammer has worked upon it the dome-shaped 'peen' has produced a number of small facets, mixing curve and angle most subtly, so that in fact the rivet end becomes an object of beauty in miniature. Alternatively, the smith may make use of what he calls a Snap. This is a monkey-tool designed to give a specific shape to the parts of the rivet that protrude from the ironwork—tapered square, hexagonal, decagonal and so forth. My own feeling, however, is that the hand-hammered rivet looks better than one which has been finished off somewhat artificially with this particular tool.

The countersunk rivet, on the other hand, is driven in so that its flat head is flush with the surface. It is unobtrusive; indeed it may after sinking be filed down in such a way that it becomes almost invisible. A different form of treatment is to hammer it so that a slight hollow, or 'dish', is made in it, the locking being affected by the outward pressure of the recessed head. But the blunt, or headless, end is of course hammered too, so that it locks securely over the other end of the hole.

It can be seen, therefore, that there is artistry as well as craftsmanship even in the relatively simple and routine job of riveting. You might have thought that this particular process offered little scope for imaginative treatment, but you would be wrong. A close parallel to this can be seen in the nail pattern in the heels of a pair of shoes. If they are cheap, mass-produced shoes then the nails are of commonplace design and set in the leather without any sort of distinction. If they are expensive, hand-made shoes the choice of nails and the pattern made with them will reveal not only skill but artistry—that of the craftsman rather than of the machine-minder.

*   *   *   *

Certain components in every gate combine the ornamental or decorative with the functional or utilitarian. In a small way the clips and even the rivets are examples of this. More obvious examples, however, are the gate 'furniture': hinges, latch, ground- or drop-bolt, for instance. Perhaps the hinge only just succeeds in meriting inclusion in this category, for in wrought-iron gates at any rate the vogue for elaborate scrolled hinges such as those on the Stillingfleet and St Albans Abbey doors no longer exists.

At first sight a gate may appear to have only one hinge; but this of course is not the case. Every gate will have two hinges at least—three if it is very tall; but one of them, referred to as the Turning-pin, may be out of sight, for it will consist of the stub-end of the back stile, carefully 'domed', turning in a cast-iron cup set in a stone block in the ground and taking the greater part of the weight.

Knuckle Assembly

The other hinge will consist of what the smith refers to as a Knuckle-assembly. This is in several parts. They consist of the Journal, a smoothly rounded section of the back stile about two inches long and six inches or so beneath the top rail, and a

pair of Flanges welded to the back stile immediately above
and below the journal. So much for the part of the knuckle-
assembly, or Hanging, on the gate itself. The remainder
of the assembly is designed for fitting into the brick or
stone gate pillar and consists of Knuckle, and Clip or
Strap. The knuckle is a short, stout piece of iron bar of the
same section as the back stile. One end of it is hollowed out
and smoothed to form a bearing for the journal shaped on the
stile. It will be semi-circular, the other half of the circle being
formed by the strap, which will be shaped to curve round the
journal and then bolted or riveted to the knuckle on each side.

The opposite end of the knuckle is deliberately left 'rough';
in fact its roughness is emphasized in order to ensure that it
can be locked immovably in the pillar. Most gate pillars, or
piers, are either of stone or of brick, and the smith must
ascertain which before he forges the hinges. There is a
reason for this. Fitting the knuckle into stone calls for one
method; fitting it into brick and mortar calls for another.
In the first case, molten lead has to be poured into a cavity
hollowed out of the stonework and then the end of the
knuckle must be forced into this. No weight or stress must be
put on the knuckle until the lead has cooled and set. In order
to increase the grip of the lead on the iron the end of the
knuckle is heated red-hot and then 'ragged' with a hot set.
This process of 'ragging' transforms the squared end of the bar
into a series of jagged teeth along its four edges. The molten
lead sets and shrinks among these, and as a result the whole
assembly of stone, lead and iron is virtually fused into one.

Lead, however, is not used, or indeed practicable, in the
case of a brick pillar. Here the knuckle will simply be set
into the mortar between one course of bricks and the next.
But in order to strengthen the grip of the drying mortar on
the iron the knuckle is first split for several inches along its
length and the two ends then splayed and twisted away from

one another, in order to offer the maximum resistance to the pull of the hinge.

With such a system of hanging—turning-pin at the base and one or more journals—a well-designed gate will swing open and close smoothly and without judder for many a long year, asking nothing more than an occasional drop of oil on the journals and a dab of grease from time to time in the cast-iron cup that supports the main weight by way of the turning-pin.

To keep it firmly closed when not in use, the gate will have two more items of furniture: the latch and the ground- or drop-bolt. The latter will also serve to hold the gate open at need. These two components offer the smith more scope for artistry and originality than the hinges do. The basic principle of a latch, of course, is rise-and-fall from and into a suitably designed catch on the opposite gate (or in the pillar opposite the hanging side in the case of a single gate). The variants on this basic principle are unlimited. Sheer weight may be used to ensure the drop of the latch; or there may be a leaf spring incorporated, or some other form of leverage. Decoration and ornament may be lavish or in-conspicuous. But the sure and easy movement of the latch, its accurate and inevitable placing in the catch intended to receive it, its freedom from sideways movement: these are factors that must never be subordinated to novelty of design. A good smith always puts first things first.

The ground-bolt, too, offers him scope for originality. It is designed not to pivot, like the latch, but to slide upwards and downwards; its vertical 'travel' is controlled by two well-judged slots, and its square or round stub-end engages accurately with a similarly shaped recess sunk into a stone block or a cast-iron plate immediately beneath the front stile, which will be duplicated elsewhere at the same radius from the hinge to hold the gate open when required. The bolt handle is frequently extended upwards to facilitate its use. It may terminate in a shapely hexagonally-forged knob, in a diminutive half-scroll, in a loose-finger ring set in a loop matching that of the latch above it. Almost certainly it will have been fashioned in such a way as to match the 'mood' of the gate as a whole.

*   *   *   *

'The gate hangs well': it is a saying with an ancient and honourable lineage. Many an inn-sign up and down the country in the form of a hanging gate testifies to this, for it carries no inscription; the image speaks eloquently for itself.

It is not only an invitation to enter the inn and partake of refreshment; it is also a tacit reminder of a tradition now many centuries old but as alive today as it was in the Golden Age of Blacksmithery: the tradition of the artist-craftsman in wrought iron—the 'magic-metal'—whose combination of strength and manifold skills ministered to the ever-growing needs of the community. It was the same whether he was called upon to forge a halfpenny nail or to fashion a masterpiece such as John Tresilian's noble Chantry Gates and Screen in St George's Chapel, Windsor, or the Davies Brothers' magnificent Chirk Castle Gates.

Many ancient crafts are succumbing today before the insidious onslaught of the machine, the assembly-line, electronics and automation. But the noblest of them all, blacksmithery—the manipulation of iron heated in the forge, held in the tongs and struck by the hammer on the anvil—survives. Under many different names, but easily recognizable for all that, Hephaestus and Vulcan, Wayland and Volundr and their fellows are at work in their smithies still. Their hammers ring out on the anvils of the New World as they formerly rang out on the anvils of the Old; and over the centuries the music they make has scarcely changed at all.

Index

Fishtail-knib, 130
Fishtail-snub-end, 129–30
Halfpenny-snub-end, 129
Leaf-end, 129
Ribbon-end, 129–30
'S'-, 128
Snub-end, 129–30
Seating, 87
Seth, 24
Setting-up, 38
Sighting, 78
Signatures, 106–7, 141
Sisera, 18
Slice, 33, 38
Smelting, 14, 34
Smith's Age, the, 26, 156
Smithy breeze, 31
Snap-heads, 151
Snaps, 152
Spills, 145
Spot-welding, 39
Stake, 43
Stamp, 75, 76
Stiles, 139, 140–1, 144, 146–7, 149
Stillingfleet Church, 108–11, 113, 153
Stockholm tar, 92
'Stone from Heaven', 24, 25, 29
Straps, 108, 110, 114, 154
Striker, 48–9, 122, 123
Superstition, 23–5, 26, 29
Swage-blocks, 54, 55, 57, 59, 61
Swages, 54, 55, 56, 123, 131, 134
Sway, 143
Syria, 14

'T'-BARS, 145
'T'-shoes, 100
Tempering, 33, 75
Tewel, 38
Tewel-iron, 38
Tijou, Jean, 118
Toe bars, 145

Tongs, 33, 49–52, 127
Close, 51
Flat, 51
Half-round, 51
Round, 51
Square, 51
Three-side, 51
Wide, 51
'Tongue' shoes, 69
Top tools, 53, 124
Tradition, 97
Tresilian, John, 156
Trinity College, Cambridge, 139
Tubal-Cain, 18, 19
Tue-iron, 38
Turning-pin, 153
Tuyère, 38
Twists, 135–8

UPSETTING, 121, 123
'Upturn' shoes, 70

VALKYRIES, the, 20
Vices, 60–1
Victoria and Albert Museum, the, 107, 113, 131, 136
Volcanoes, 18
Volundr, 20–1, 156
Vulcan, 18, 19, 23, 46, 131, 156

WALL, 102, 103
Water-leaves, 144
Wayland the Smith, 19, 46, 131, 156
Welding, 37, 120–3
Westminster Abbey, 116
Wieland, 20
Wind, 143, 148
Windsor, 156

ZEUS, 15, 16, 17